# PE

## electrical and computer engineering

## electrical and electronics

*practice exam*

**NCEES**
*advancing licensure for engineers and surveyors*

978-1-932613-55-1

ISBN 978-1-932613-55-1

Printed in the United States of America
November 2014

# CONTENTS

## About NCEES

The National Council of Examiners for Engineering and Surveying (NCEES) is a nonprofit organization made up of engineering and surveying licensing boards from all U.S. states and territories. Since its founding in 1920, NCEES has been committed to advancing licensure for engineers and surveyors in order to protect the health, safety, and welfare of the American public.

NCEES helps its member licensing boards carry out their duties to regulate the professions of engineering and surveying. It develops best-practice models for state licensure laws and regulations and promotes uniformity among the states. It develops and administers the exams used for engineering and surveying licensure throughout the country. It also provides services to help licensed engineers and surveyors practice their professions in other U.S. states and territories.

## Updates on exam content and procedures

Visit us at **ncees.org/exams** for updates on everything exam-related, including specifications, exam-day policies, scoring, and corrections to published exam preparation materials. This is also where you will register for the exam and find additional steps you should follow in your state to be approved for the exam.

## Exam-day schedule

Be sure to arrive at the exam site on time. Late-arriving examinees will not be allowed into the exam room once the proctor has begun to read the exam script. The report time for the exam will be printed on your Exam Authorization. Normally, you will be given 1 hour between morning and afternoon sessions.

## Admission to the exam site

To be admitted to the exam, you must bring two items: (1) your Exam Authorization and (2) a current, signed, government-issued identification.

## Examinee Guide

The *NCEES Examinee Guide* is the official guide to policies and procedures for all NCEES exams. All examinees are required to read this document before starting the exam registration process. You can download it at ncees.org/exams. It is your responsibility to make sure that you have the current version.

NCEES exams are administered in either a computer-based format or a pencil-and-paper format. Each method of administration has specific rules. This guide describes the rules for each exam format. Refer to the appropriate section for your exam.

## Scoring and reporting

NCEES typically releases exam results to its member licensing boards 8–10 weeks after the exam. Depending on your state, you will be notified of your exam result online through your MyNCEES account or via postal mail from your state licensing board. Detailed information on the scoring process can be found at ncees.org/exams.

## Staying connected

To keep up to date with NCEES announcements, events, and activities, connect with us on your preferred social media network.

**NCEES Principles and Practice of Engineering Examination**
**ELECTRICAL AND COMPUTER—ELECTRICAL AND ELECTRONICS Exam Specifications**
**Effective Beginning with the April 2009 Examinations**

- The exam is an 8-hour open-book exam. It contains 40 multiple-choice questions in the 4-hour morning session, and 40 multiple-choice questions in the 4-hour afternoon session. Examinee works all questions.

- The exam uses both the International System of units (SI) and the US Customary System (USCS).

- The exam is developed with questions that will require a variety of approaches and methodologies including design, analysis, and application. Some questions may require knowledge of engineering economics.

- The knowledge areas specified as examples of kinds of knowledge are not exclusive or exhaustive categories.

|  | Approximate Number of Questions |
|---|---|
| **I. General Electrical Engineering Knowledge** | **40** |
| A. Circuit Analysis | 20 |
|    1. Passive components | |
|    2. DC circuits | |
|    3. Sinusoidal analysis | |
|    4. Transient analysis | |
|    5. Power and energy calculations | |
|    6. Battery characteristics and ratings | |
|    7. Power supply | |
| B. Measurement and Instrumentation | 8 |
|    1. Transducer and system characteristics | |
|    2. Data evaluation | |
|    3. Operational amplifiers | |
| C. Safety and Design Limits | 3 |
|    1. Interface applications | |
|    2. Failure limits and circuit protection | |
|    3. Safety grounding | |
|    4. Electromagnetic interference and exposure | |
|    5. Reliability | |
|    6. Electric shock and burns | |
| D. Signal Processing | 9 |
|    1. Sampling theory (aliasing, Nyquist sampling rate) | |
|    2. Transforms and applications | |
|    3. Analog-to-digital (A/D) and digital-to-analog (D/A) conversions | |
| **II. Digital Systems** | **9** |
| A. Digital Logic | 4 |
|    1. Boolean algebra | |
|    2. Combinational and sequential logic | |

B. Digital Components    5
   1. Digital devices
   2. Memory devices
   3. Programmable logic devices
   4. Microcontrollers/embedded systems

**III. Electric and Magnetic Field Theory and Applications**    **7**

A. Electromagnetic Fields    3
   1. Theory
   2. EMI/EMC
B. Transmission Lines and Guided Waves    2
   1. Transmission lines, balanced and unbalanced
   2. Waveguides
C. Antennas    2
   1. Gain, patterns, and polarization
   2. Impedance

**IV. Electronics**    **10**

A. Electronic Circuit Theory    5
   1. Small-signal and large-signal models
   2. Active networks and filters
   3. Nonlinear circuits (e.g., comparators)
   4. Sinusoidal steady-state analysis
   5. Transient analysis
   6. Power and energy calculations
B. Electronic Components and Circuits    5
   1. Solid-state power devices and power electronics
      applications
   2. Battery characteristics and ratings
   3. Power supplies
   4. Oscillators and phase-locked loop characteristics
   5. Amplifiers
   6. Modulators and demodulators
   7. Diodes
   8. Circuit protection and safety
   9. Transistors and applications

**V. Control System Fundamentals**    **6**

A. Block diagrams
B. Characteristic equations
C. Frequency response
D. Time response
E. Control system design and implementation (e.g., compensators,
   steady-state error)
F. Stability (e.g., tests, Bode plots, root locus, transport delay)

## VI. Communications     8

  A. Modulation     3
     1. Analog modulation
     2. Digital modulation
     3. Spread spectrum modulation characteristics

  B. Noise and Interference     2
     1. Signal-to-noise ratio
     2. Quantization noise
     3. Noise figure and temperature
     4. Interference
     5. Coding, error detection and correction

  C. Telecommunications     3
     1. Wireline communications
     2. Wireless communications
     3. Optical communications
     4. Multiplexing
     5. Traffic and switching

# ELECTRICAL AND ELECTRONICS AM PRACTICE EXAM

**101.** For the circuit in the figure, $v_1(t) = 10 \cos(400t)$ V. The maximum value of the current (amperes) in the capacitor will be most nearly:

(A) 0.12
(B) 0.21
(C) 0.87
(D) 1.01

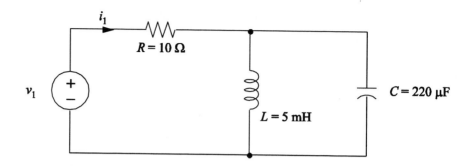

**102.** The figure shows the "pi-pad" configuration for a 3-dB attenuator matched to a 50-$\Omega$ system. Which option best represents the $y$ parameters for this 2-port circuit in the form [$Y_{11}$, $Y_{12}$; $Y_{21}$, $Y_{22}$]?

(A) [0.0065, 0.0069; 0.0069, 0.0065]
(B) [0.056, −0.059; −0.059, 0.056]
(C) [0.059, 0.056; 0.056, 0.059]
(D) [0.059, −0.056; −0.056, 0.059]

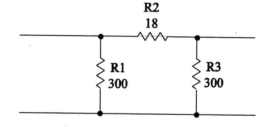

*pg 29-15 of rE manual*

**103.** Tests at two terminals of a linear network produce the following:

1. with the terminals shorted, the current in the short circuit is 3.0 A.

2. with a conductance of 0.2 S connected to the terminals, the voltage between the terminals is 5 V.

The linear network may be replaced by a current source (amperes) in parallel with a conductance (S) of most nearly:

| | Current | Conductance |
|---|---|---|
| (A) | 1.0 | 0.2 |
| (B) | 3.0 | 0.4 |
| (C) | 2.0 | 0.6 |
| (D) | 3.0 | 0.6 |

✓ **104.** **Figure 1** represents equivalent transformations of the components in **Figure 2**. The values of the transformed source and resistor in **Figure 1** are most nearly:

|  | $I_A$ | $G_B$ |
|---|---|---|
| (A) | −2.5 A | 0.25 S |
| (B) | 2.5 A | 0.25 S |
| (C) | 2.5 A | 1.0 S |
| (D) | 1.25 A | 0.5 S |

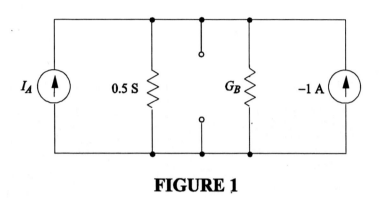

**FIGURE 1**

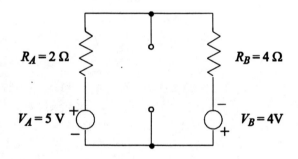

**FIGURE 2**

*Current Source*
*transformation*

√ **105.** The switch in the figure below has been closed for a long time. At $t = 0$ it is opened. The equation for the voltage $v(t)$, for $t > 0$, is of the form $v(t) = A + Be^{-t/\tau}$. The values of $A$, $B$, and $\tau$ are most nearly:

|     | $\underline{A}$ | $\underline{B}$ | $\underline{\tau}$ |
|-----|------|------|-------|
| (A) | 4 V  | 2 V  | 6 ms  |
| (B) | 0 V  | 4 V  | 3 ms  |
| (C) | 0 V  | 6 V  | 6 ms  |
| (D) | 0 V  | 4 V  | 6 ms  |

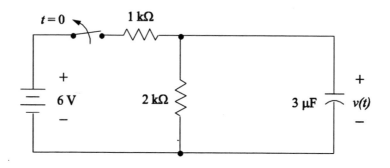

√ **106.** In the circuit below, Switch S1 closes at $t = 0$. The diode D is rated at a maximum peak current of 5 A. Assume that the initial charge on the capacitor is zero. The minimum value of $R$ ($\Omega$) to prevent exceeding the diode maximum peak current is most nearly:

(A) 33
(B) 24
(C) 21
(D) 11

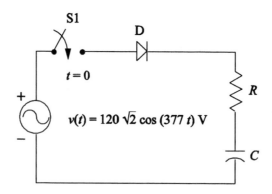

$v(t) = 120\sqrt{2}\cos(377\,t)\ \text{V}$

**107.** A current $i(t) = [5 \cos(\omega t) + 2 \cos(2\omega t)]$ A flows through a 3-$\Omega$ resistor. The average power (W) absorbed by the 3-$\Omega$ resistor is most nearly:

(A) 44
(B) 74
(C) 87
(D) 147

$$\hat{i}_{avg} = \sqrt{\left(\frac{5}{1.41}\right)^2 + \left(\frac{2}{1.41}\right)^2}$$

$$p = i^2 R$$

**108.** A sinusoidal voltage of $v(t) = [50 \cos(\omega t + 45°) + 28.28 \cos(\omega t)]$ V is applied across a 5-$\Omega$ resistor. The average power (W) delivered to the resistor is most nearly:

(A) 330
(B) 530
(C) 660
(D) 1,225

$$Avg\,V \quad \frac{50\angle 45 + 28.28\angle 0}{1.41}$$

$$\frac{V^2}{R} \approx 533$$

**109.** This question investigates the design of a series-regulated power supply, shown in **Figure 1**, using a conventional 5-V series regulator. Assume the load ($R_{LOAD}$) is purely resistive and that negligible current passes through a series regulator common ground connection.

**Figure 2** shows the case temperature dissipation derating curve for the series regulator. The junction/case thermal resistance for the series regulator is given in the figure.

Assume $V_{IN} = 14$ V, $R_{LOAD} = 5$ Ω, with a heat sink applied to the case. The maximum permissible case temperature under these conditions is most nearly:

(A)     110°C
(B)     112°C
(C)     114°C
(D)     116°C

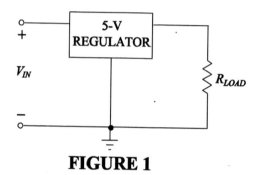

**FIGURE 1**

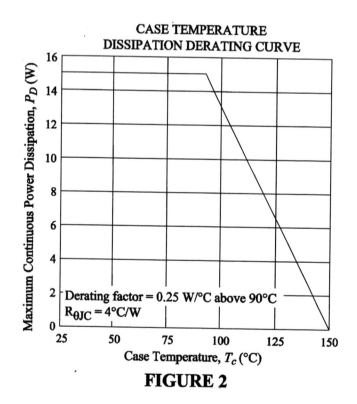

**FIGURE 2**

**110.** Three 30-μF capacitors are connected in star (Y) form between the terminals A, B, C and a junction point N as shown in the figure. The capacitance (μF) between terminals A and B is most nearly:

(A)   2/30
(B)   15
(C)   60
(D)   90

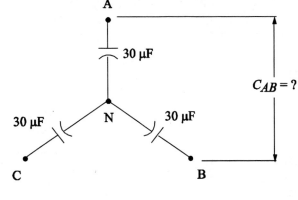

**111.** This question investigates the performance of the temperature measurement circuit shown below. The temperature sensor is linear, with the following open-circuit voltages:

$V_S = 0$ mV at 0°C
$V_S = -100$ mV at 100°C

The operational amplifier (op amp) is ideal.

At 100°C, the maximum output voltage at $V_o$ (V) due to the tolerance in $R_2$ is most nearly:

(A)   2.5
(B)   5.2
(C)   10.1
(D)   15.3

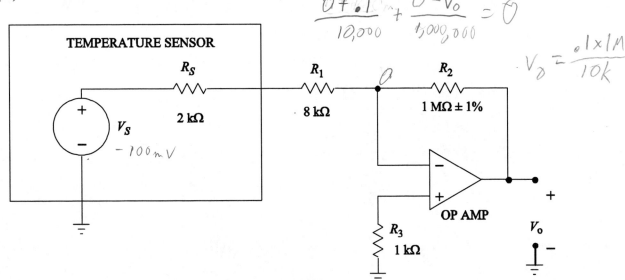

**112.** Which of the following regression models is **not** considered to be a linear regression model for predicting $\hat{Y}$ in terms of $X$?

(A) $\hat{Y} = b_0 + b_1 X_1$

(B) $\hat{Y} = b_0 + b_1 X_1 + b_2 X_2^2$

(C) $\hat{Y} = b_0 + b_1 X_1 + b_2 X_2 + b_{12} X_1 X_2$

(D) $\hat{Y} = b_0 + b_1 X_1^{b_2}$

**113.** Assume the op-amp in the circuit shown is ideal. In order that $V_{out} = K(V_1 - V_2)$, where K is a constant, the following relationship between resistors must be true:

(A) $(R_1 + R_2) = (R_3 + R_4)$

(B) $(R_1 + R_3) = (R_2 + R_4)$

(C) $\dfrac{R_1}{R_2} = \dfrac{R_3}{R_4}$

(D) $\dfrac{R_1}{R_4} = \dfrac{R_3}{R_2}$

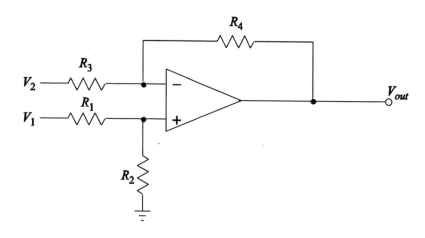

**114.** The Bode plot for the circuit shown for $G(\omega) = \dfrac{V_2(\omega)}{V_1(\omega)}$ is most nearly:

$\dfrac{V_2 - 0}{\frac{1}{sC}} = \dfrac{0 - V_1}{R}$

$\dfrac{V_2}{V_1} = -\dfrac{1}{sCR}$

$= \dfrac{1}{CR\omega} j$

**(A)**

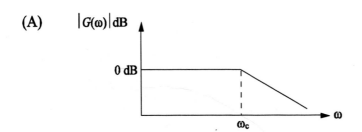

**(B)**

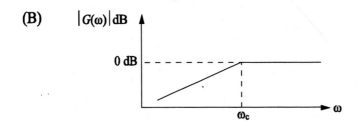

**(C)**

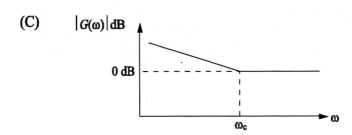

**(D)**

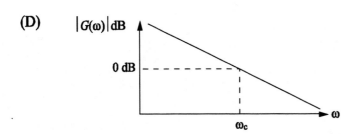

**115.** Two components of a system are connected in parallel. The probability of survival (reliability) $R$ of each of the components making up the system is given below.

| Component | Reliability |
|-----------|-------------|
| $R_1$ | 0.92 |
| $R_2$ | 0.85 |

The combined system works properly if either one of the parallel components functions. The reliability of the combined system (parallel combination) is most nearly:

(A)  0.78
(B)  0.85
(C)  0.92
(D)  0.99

**116.** According to the Nyquist sampling theorem, a sufficient condition for there to be no aliasing in the sampled signal is that the highest frequency in the signal prior to sampling must be:

(A)  less than half of the sampling frequency

(B)  greater than half of the sampling frequency

(C)  less than the sampling frequency

(D)  greater than the sampling frequency

**117.** Given a pulse transfer function of:

$$\frac{1}{z^{-1}\left(1 - 0.7z^{-1}\right)}$$

The finite pole(s) in the $z$-plane is/are:

(A)  0 and 0.7

(B)  0 and 1/0.7

(C)  0.7

(D)  1/0.7

**118.** The microprocessor-based data acquisition system shown samples an analog signal, processes it digitally, and then converts the processed signal back to analog form. The system uses data converter circuits with the following characteristics:

A/D:   4-bit offset binary, unity gain, bipolar –5 V to +5 V; –5 V corresponds to $(0000)_2$

D/A:   4-bit offset binary, unity gain, unipolar, 0 V to +10 V; 0 V corresponds to $(0000)_2$

For an input voltage of +2.0 V, the A/D converter output code is most nearly:

(A)   $(0011)_2$
(B)   $(0100)_2$
(C)   $(1011)_2$
(D)   $(1101)_2$

**119.** If $X(s) = \dfrac{s+6}{s(s+2)(s+3)}$, then the corresponding initial value of the signal $x(t)$ as $t$ approaches

0 is most nearly:

(A)   0
(B)   1
(C)   6
(D)   $\infty$

$$\lim_{t \to 0} x(t) = \lim_{s \to \infty} sF(s) \quad \frac{s+6}{s^2+5s+6}$$

$$\text{derivative} \to \frac{1}{2s+5}$$

$$\lim = 0$$

**120.** A biomedical signal is sampled at 128 Hz. No anti-aliasing filter is used. Spectral analysis on the sampled data shows a strong source at 58 Hz that was not in the original signal. The most likely source of the 58-Hz component is:

(A) random noise in the original signal

(B) a power line artifact picked up by the equipment

(C) a 70-Hz source in the original signal

(D) a 122-Hz source in the original signal

**121.** The function $F = (\overline{A} + B)(\overline{B} + \overline{C})(A + C)$ can be expressed as the following sum of products:

(A) $F = ABC + A\overline{B}C$

(B) $F = ABC + \overline{A}\,\overline{B}C$

(C) $F = AB\overline{C} + A\overline{B}C$

(D) $F = AB\overline{C} + \overline{A}\,\overline{B}C$

**122.** The output $D$ in the circuit is:

(A) $B(A + C)$

(B) $(A + B)(B + C)$

(C) $\overline{A}\overline{B} + \overline{B}\overline{C}$

(D) $(\overline{A} + \overline{B})CB$

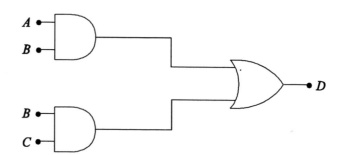

**123.** An engineer chooses open-collector output TTL technology to provide sufficient current to drive a device. The circuit shown is implemented with a 7405 package and corresponds to the following logic function (assume that a logic-0 corresponds to 0 V):

(A) AND
(B) NAND
(C) OR
(D) NOR

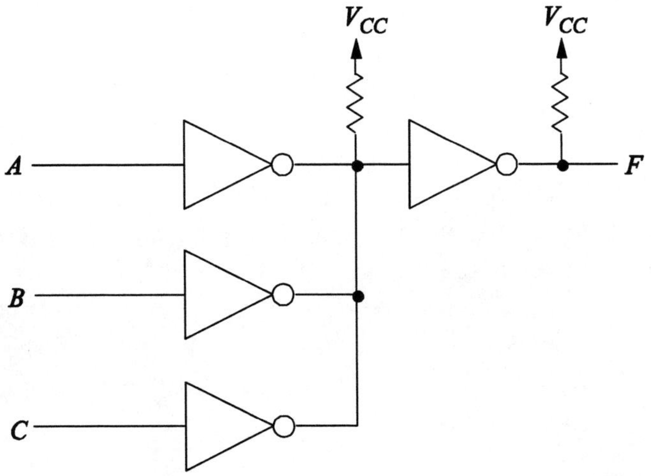


**124.** A 16-bit floating point word has the format shown below.

0 1 0 0

| Byte 0 | | | | | | | | Byte 1 | | | | | | | |
|---|---|---|---|---|---|---|---|---|---|---|---|---|---|---|---|
| 7 | 6 | 5 | 4 | 3 | 2 | 1 | 0 | 7 | 6 | 5 | 4 | 3 | 2 | 1 | 0 |
| S | E | | | | | | | M | | | | | | | |
| MSb | | | | | | | LSb | MSb | | | | | | | LSb |

In the table, S is a sign bit with S = 1 indicating a value less than zero; E is a 7-bit excess-64 exponent of a power of 2; and M is an 8-bit mantissa that is a fractional part of unity. MSb and LSb denote the most significant and least significant bits of each part of the word. A 16-bit word corresponding to $(4000)_{16}$ represents a numeric value that is most nearly:

(A) 0.0
(B) 0.5
(C) 1.0
(D) 2.0

M=0
E=1000000=64
Exp= E-64=0
M×2° =0

**125.** A dc current of 50 A is flowing in a long isolated wire. The magnitude of the magnetic field intensity, $\overline{H}$ (A/m), 10 cm from the center of the wire is most nearly:

(A) 0.001
(B) 8
(C) 80
(D) 250

**126.** A basic Time-Domain Reflectometry (TDR) system is used with an oscilloscope to display the waveform at the input end of a line driven by an alternating 0–1 square waveform signal in a non-return-to-zero (NRZ) digital system.

A 1,000-m cable is terminated with a short circuit at the far end. The first reflected wave appears 9.43 μs after the incident waveform. The actual velocity in the cable divided by the speed of light is most nearly:

(A) 0.35
(B) 0.71
(C) 1.0
(D) 1.41

**127.** The radiation pattern of a wire of length $L$ (centered at $x = 0$, $y = 0$, and $z = 0$) is shown in the figure. The pattern is normalized such that the magnitude of radiation is one in the direction of maximum radiation. The wire is located along the $y$-axis of the radiation pattern as shown by the broader line. The wire has a time-varying current distribution along its length. The current distribution that would give the pattern shown is most nearly:

(A) $I_o \cos\left(\dfrac{\pi y}{L}\right)$

(B) $I_o \cos\left(\dfrac{3\pi y}{L}\right)$

(C) $I_o \cos\left(\dfrac{5\pi y}{L}\right)$

(D) $I_o \cos\left(\dfrac{7\pi y}{L}\right)$

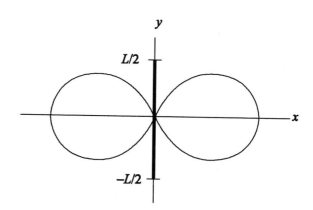

**128.** In a communication system, Transmission Line A and Transmission Line B will be matched by using a short-circuited lossless stub connected at Point X. The characteristic impedance of the stub is 75 Ω. The admittance at Point X before the stub is connected or Transmission Line A is connected is found to be $(0.02 + j0.04)$ S. The characteristic impedance of Transmission Line A is 50 Ω. The wavelength of the transmitter carrier is $\lambda = 0.8$ m. The length (mm) of the stub that will produce the desired impedance of 50 Ω at Point X is most nearly:

(A)   17
(B)   21
(C)   41
(D)   46

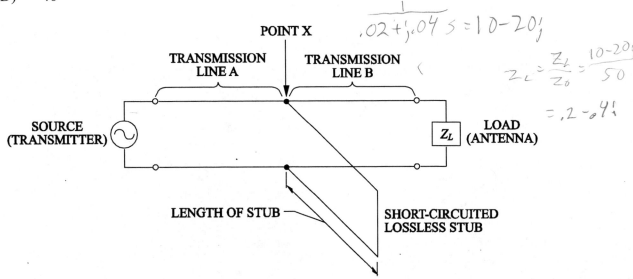

**129.** Consider the following circuit with an N-Channel enhancement mode MOSFET:

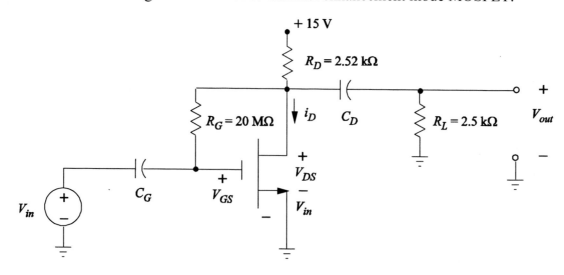

$C_D$ and $C_G$ are infinitely large.

The small signal model for the FET is:

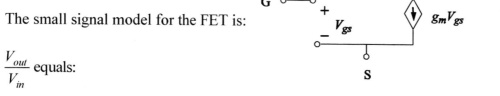

$\dfrac{V_{out}}{V_{in}}$ equals:

(A) $\dfrac{-g_m R_G}{1 - \dfrac{R_G}{R_D} - \dfrac{R_G}{R_L}}$

(B) $\dfrac{1 - g_m R_G}{1 - \dfrac{R_G}{R_D} - \dfrac{R_G}{R_L}}$

(C) $\dfrac{-g_m R_G}{1 + \dfrac{R_G}{R_D} + \dfrac{R_G}{R_L}}$

(D) $\dfrac{1 - g_m R_G}{1 + \dfrac{R_G}{R_D} + \dfrac{R_G}{R_L}}$

**130.** The transfer function $A_v(s)$ of an active filter is given by

$$A_v(s) = \frac{-10^6 s}{s^2 + 10^5 s + 10^{12}}$$

The 3-dB bandwidth (rad/s) is most nearly:

*[handwritten annotations: $\omega^2$, "w is center freq", "BW"]*

(A) $1 \times 10^5$
(B) $2 \times 10^5$
(C) $5 \times 10^5$
(D) $1 \times 10^6$

**131.** An electrochemical cell exhibits the nonlinear *V-I* characteristic shown in **Figure 1** and is used in the circuit shown in **Figure 2**.

The output voltage $V_o$ (V) in **Figure 2** is most nearly:

(A)  2.0
(B)  4.0
(C)  6.0
(D)  8.0

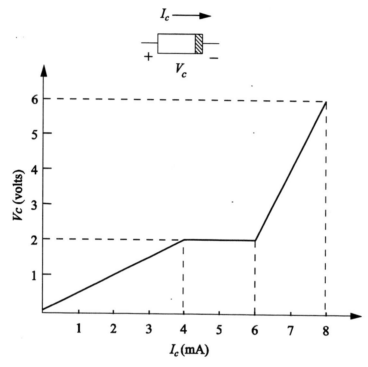

**FIGURE 1**

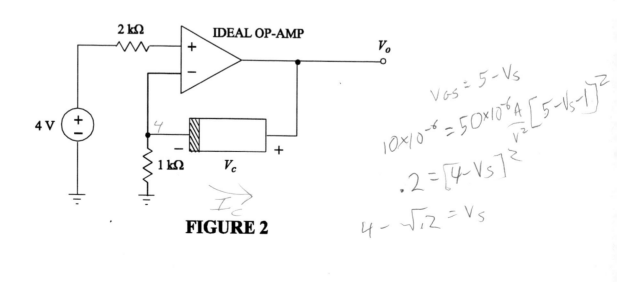

**FIGURE 2**

$V_{GS} = 5 - V_S$

$10 \times 10^{-6} = 50 \times 10^{-6} \dfrac{A}{V^2} [5 - V_S - 1]^2$

$.2 = [4 - V_S]^2$

$4 - \sqrt{.2} = V_S$

**GO ON TO THE NEXT PAGE**

**132.** Consider the oscillator circuit shown below. This circuit uses which resonant mode(s) of the crystal X1?

(A)  Series resonant

(B)  Parallel resonant

(C)  Series-parallel resonant

(D)  Not resonant

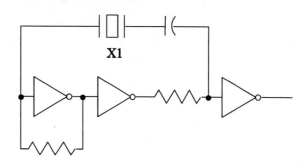

**133.** Consider the MOSFET degenerated current mirror shown below having input current $I_X$ and output current $I_Z$. The MOSFETs have the following characteristics:

- Identical electrical characteristics
- Threshold voltages of 1 V
- Infinite drain output resistance ($R_{DS}$)
- Operate within their saturated region of operation

All current sources are ideal.

In the saturation region, $I_D = K[V_{GS} - V_T]^2$ where $K = 50$ μA/V$^2$ for each MOSFET.

Assuming $I_Z = 10$ μA and the voltage at node X is 5 V, the resistance (kΩ) of resistor $R$ is most nearly:

(A)  52
(B)  118
(C)  237
(D)  355

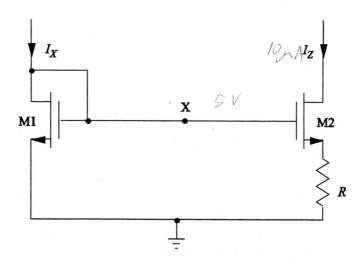

134. The transfer function $Y/R$ for the block diagram shown below is:

(A) $\dfrac{G_1 G_2}{1 + G_2 H_2} + G_4$

(B) $\dfrac{G_1 G_2}{1 - G_2 H_2} + G_4$

(C) $G_1 + \dfrac{G_2}{1 + G_2 H_2} + G_4$

(D) $\dfrac{G_1 G_2 G_4}{1 + G_2 H_2}$

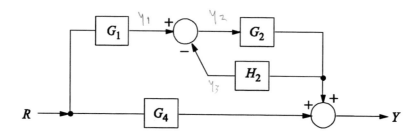

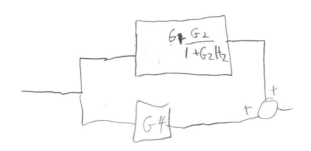

$$\frac{G_1 G_2}{1 + G_2 H_2} + G_4$$

**135.** The control system in the figure is to be formulated in state variable form. The generalized equations for the state variable formulation are:

$$\frac{dx(t)}{dt} = Ax(t) + Bu(t)$$  I.  State equation

$$y(t) = Cx(t)$$  II.  Output equation

The state variables are to be defined as $x(t) = x_1(t)$, $dx(t)/dt = x_2(t)$.

Let the state matrix $A$ in equation I be defined as

$$\begin{bmatrix} 0 & 1 \\ -6 & -3 \end{bmatrix}$$

Using the $A$ matrix as defined, what is the matrix $C$?

(A)  $[1 \quad 4]$

(B)  $\begin{bmatrix} 1 \\ 4 \end{bmatrix}$

(C)  $[4 \quad 1]$

(D)  $\begin{bmatrix} 4 \\ 1 \end{bmatrix}$

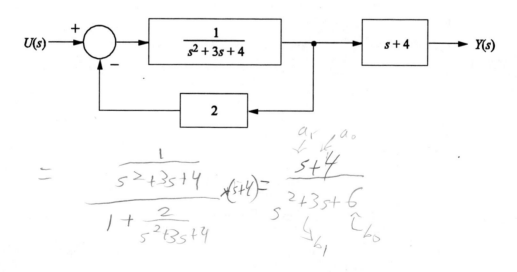

136. **Figure 1** shows the magnitude (dB) of the open-loop transfer function of a feedback control system as a function of frequency, and **Figure 2** shows the phase of the open-loop transfer function as a function of frequency.

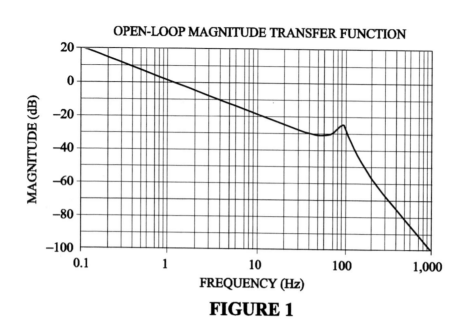

OPEN-LOOP MAGNITUDE TRANSFER FUNCTION

**FIGURE 1**

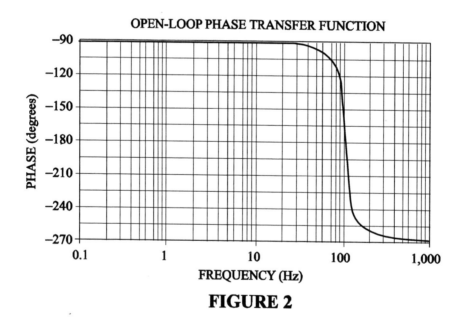

OPEN-LOOP PHASE TRANSFER FUNCTION

**FIGURE 2**

**136.** **(Continued)**

The open-loop poles of the system are most like which of the following s-plane figures?

**(A)**

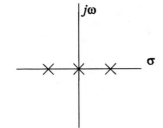

**(B)**

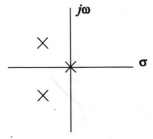

**(C)**

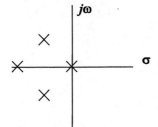

**(D)**

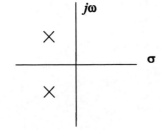

**137.** Consider the voltage waveform $x(t)$, which is the output of an amplitude-modulated (AM) transmitter:

$$x(t) = 40 \cos (200{,}000\pi\, t) + 10 \cos (197{,}000\pi\, t) + 10 \cos (203{,}000\pi\, t)$$

The percentage of modulation of the AM waveform, $x(t)$, is most nearly:

(A)   25%
(B)   33%
(C)   50%
(D)   75%

**138.** Consider the three-stage r-f amplifier shown below. AR1 refers to the input amplifier stage, AR2 to the second stage, and AR3 to the output stage.

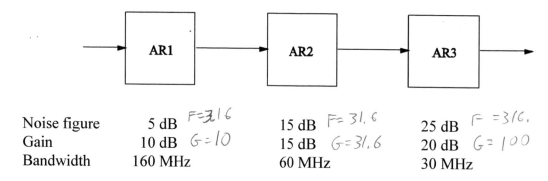

| | AR1 | AR2 | AR3 |
|---|---|---|---|
| Noise figure | 5 dB $F=3.16$ | 15 dB $F=31.6$ | 25 dB $F=316.$ |
| Gain | 10 dB $G=10$ | 15 dB $G=31.6$ | 20 dB $G=100$ |
| Bandwidth | 160 MHz | 60 MHz | 30 MHz |

For this amplifier configuration, the total noise figure (dB) is most nearly:

(A)   5.0
(B)   6.6
(C)   8.6
(D)   12.3

$$F_1 + \frac{F_2-1}{G_1} + \frac{F_3-1}{G_1 G_2} + \frac{F_4-1}{G_1 G_2 G_3} + \ldots$$

$$NF = 10 \cdot \log F$$
$$5\,db = 10 \log F$$
$$.5 = \log F$$
$$10^{.5} = F$$

$$F = 7.221$$
$$NF = 10 \log 7.221 = 8.6$$

**139.** Digital telecommunication equipment provides connection-oriented AND/OR connectionless service. Connection-oriented service is provided by:

    (A)    ATM

    (B)    ETHERNET

    (C)    FDDI

    (D)    SMDS

**140.** A transmitter operating at 23.6 GHz has a power output of 20 mW. A receiver is located 8 miles from the transmitter. The free space attenuation (dB) is most nearly:

    (A)    142

    (B)    124

    (C)    119

    (D)    115

This completes the morning session. Solutions begin on page 53.

# ELECTRICAL AND ELECTRONICS PM PRACTICE EXAM

**501.** Referring to the figure, the peak voltage (V) across the 50-Ω resistor is most nearly:

(A) 35
(B) 51
(C) 71
(D) 92

$\omega L j = 0.2 \times 2\pi \times 160 = 201 j$

$-j\frac{1}{\omega C} = -249 j$

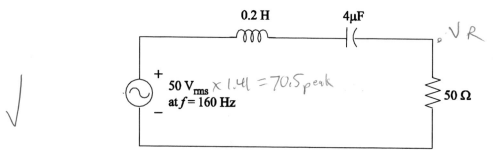

0.2 H          4µF
                    ∘ VR

$+$
50 V_rms × 1.41 = 70.5 peak
at f = 160 Hz          50 Ω
$-$

$$\frac{50}{50 - 48 j} \times (70.5 \angle 0) = 50.8 \angle 43.8°$$

**502.** In the following circuit, the switch has been closed for a very long time before $t = 0$. At $t = 0$, the switch is opened. The value of the voltage $v$ (V) just after the switch is opened ($t = 0^+$) is most nearly:

(A) −5,000
(B) 0
(C) 12
(D) 5,000

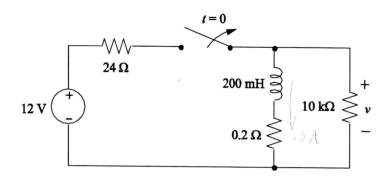

$t = 0$

24 Ω

200 mH

12 V

10 kΩ    $+$    $v$

0.2 Ω   .5 A        $-$

**503.** The elements in **Figure 1** and **Figure 2** are linear and the sources are dc. The voltage source $V_S$ (V dc) and the resistor $R$ ($\Omega$) in **Figure 2**, equivalent to **Figure 1** external to terminals $a$-$b$, are most nearly:

|     | $V_S$ | $R$ |
|-----|-------|-----|
| (A) | −22   | 4   |
| (B) | −22   | 7   |
| (C) | −21   | 7   |
| (D) | 10    | 4   |

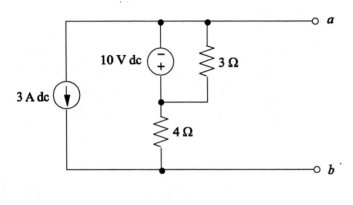

**FIGURE 1**

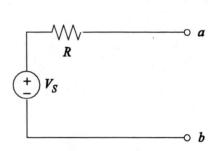

**FIGURE 2**

**504.** Referring to the figure, the voltage $v(t)$ (V) across the current source $2e^{-t}$ is most nearly (hint: use superposition to save time):

(A) $(20 + 24e^{-t})/3$

(B) $(20 - 24e^{-t})/3$

(C) $(60 + 108e^{-t})/9$

(D) $(60 - 108e^{-t})/9$

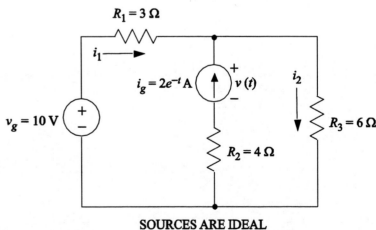

SOURCES ARE IDEAL

**505.** In the figure below, the **average** voltage $V_o$ (V) across the 0.022-µF capacitor is most nearly:

    (A)  1.7
    (B)  2.2
    (C)  4.3
    (D)  5.0

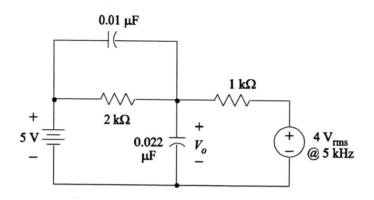

**506.** A communications system consists of a source operating at 1 MHz and a load. The source and the load can be modeled by the lumped-parameter circuit shown. The value of $Z_L$ that will permit maximum power transfer from the source to the load is most nearly:

    (A)  a resistor of 600 Ω

    (B)  a resistor of 600 Ω in series with a capacitor of 0.02 µF

    (C)  a resistor of 600 Ω in series with a capacitor of 500 pF

    (D)  a resistor of 600 Ω in series with an inductor of 50 µH

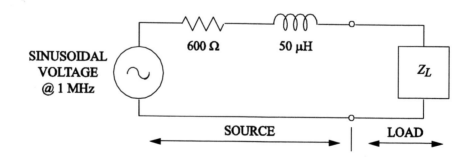

**507.** A BJT transistor has a maximum power dissipation of 4 W at an ambient temperature of 30°C, and a maximum junction temperature of 150°C. The device is operating with an ambient temperature of 30°C and is dissipating 1.5 W. The junction temperature of the device is most nearly:

(A)   45°C
(B)   75°C
(C)   86°C
(D)   120°C

**508.** A resistance $R = 10\ \Omega$, an inductance $L = 20$ H, and a capacitor $C$ are connected in parallel as shown in the figure. If the magnitude of current $I$ drawn from the source voltage is minimum at a frequency of $f = 100/2\pi$ Hz, the capacitor $C$ has a value (μF) of most nearly:

(A)   0.5
(B)   5.0
(C)   100
(D)   50π

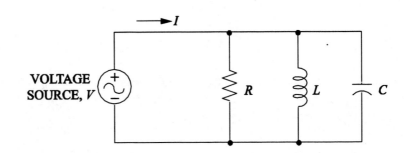

**509.** Two coils, connected in series, are wound in the same direction. Each coil has a self-inductance of 4 H. If the coefficient of coupling is 0.75 for mutual inductance, the equivalent inductance (H) of the series combination is most nearly:

(A)   2
(B)   8
(C)   11
(D)   14

**510.** A 20-V battery having an unknown internal resistance is switched into a series RC network having $R = 0.5\ \Omega$ and $C = 1$ F. Assume the capacitor is initially uncharged. If the capacitor voltage rises to 10 V in 1 sec, the value $(\Omega)$ of the unknown resistance is most nearly:

    (A)    1.4
    (B)    0.9
    (C)    0.5
    (D)    0.1

*pg 31-8*

**511.** A real-time data-acquisition system receives mechanical position input data that is limited to a maximum movement frequency of 10 Hz. The input signal varies between –5 V and +5 V. The sample rate is 100 samples per second.

It is desired to design a slew rate check on the input data that will detect any sample that differs from its predecessor by more than would be possible for a 5-V peak, 10-Hz sinusoidal signal. The maximum rate of change for a sine wave occurs as the signal crosses the zero axis. The maximum change (V) for a single sample, as compared to its predecessor, that can be permitted by the rate check software is most nearly:

    (A)    0.05
    (B)    0.314
    (C)    3.14
    (D)    5.0

$$5\sin(2\pi 10 t)$$

$$\frac{dV}{dt} = 314\cos(2\pi 10 t)$$

$$\frac{dV}{dt} = 314\cos(62.8\ t)\quad @\ t=0\quad \frac{dV}{dt} = 314$$

$$dt = .01\ s$$

$$\Delta V = 314 \times .01 = 3.14\ V$$

**512.** For the circuit shown, $V_{out}$ is most nearly:

(A) $4\angle-90°\ V_{in}$

(B) $4\angle90°\ V_{in}$

(C) $(1-j4)\ V_{in}$

(D) $(1+j4)\ V_{in}$

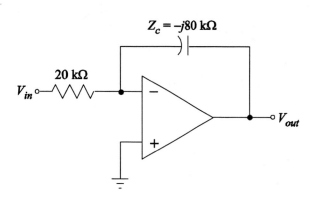

**513.** An ac voltmeter with a full-scale range of 5 V is used to measure the output voltage of an amplifier. The amplifier has an output impedance of 2,000 $\Omega$, and the meter has a sensitivity of 2,000 $\Omega$/V. When connected to the amplifier, the meter reads 2.5 V. If a different meter with a sensitivity of 100,000 $\Omega$/V and a full-scale range of 5 V is connected to the amplifier, the voltmeter reading (V) will be most nearly:

(A) 2.1

(B) 3

(C) 3.6

(D) 5

**514.** For the 4-wire RTD circuit shown, which of the following would cause the greatest measurement error in $V_{sense}$?

(A)    Increase lead A resistance by 2 Ω.

(B)    Increase lead B resistance by 3 Ω.

(C)    Increase lead D resistance by 3 Ω.

(D)    Current source $I$ has a 1% error.

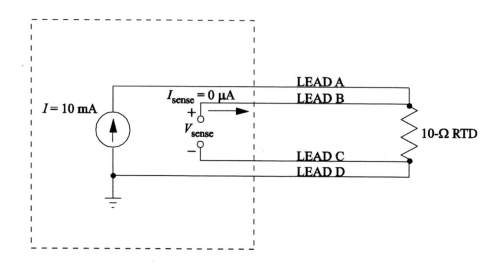

**515.** The circuit shown models a two-stage amplifier. The amplifier's output is transformer-coupled to a display that has an input resistance of 15 Ω. Voltages and currents are rms values. Transformer T may be considered ideal (lossless).

If the P:S turns ratio of T is 3:1, and the maximum value of $I_2$ is 187.5 mA$_{rms}$, then the minimum rating of T (volt-amperes) is most nearly:

(A)    0.70
(B)    0.76
(C)    3.0
(D)    8.5

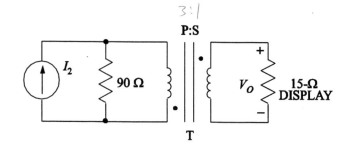

**516.** An audio signal will be digitized for transmission. If the channel capacity is 400k bps and the signal-to-noise ratio of the receiver is 15 dB, then the Shannon bandwidth (kHz) is most nearly:

(A)     80
(B)     100
(C)     115
(D)     265

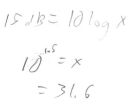

$15 dB = 10 \log x$

$10^{1.5} = x$

$= 31.6$

**517.** In a Laplace transform, a transport delay T can best be described as:

(A)     inconsequential to the overall stability of the system

(B)     useful because it improves the overall stability of the system

(C)     providing a voltage lag that increases exponentially with frequency

(D)     detrimental to the overall stability of the system

**518.** The third harmonic of the Fourier series for the waveform in the figure has a frequency (Hz) of:

(A)     250
(B)     750
(C)     4,712
(D)     The third harmonic does not exist.

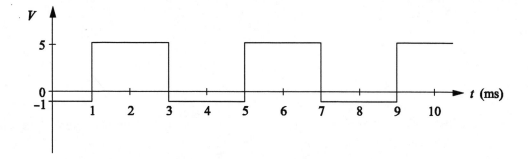

**519.** A waveform having period $T = 2$ is described by a constant value of 10 over the interval $0 < t < 1$ and zero over the interval $1 < t < 2$. This signal is repeated continually for all time $t$. The first terms of the trigonometric Fourier series are most nearly:

(A) $5.0 + 6.4 \cos (3.14 \, t) + 2.1 \cos (9.42 \, t) + \ldots$

(B) $5.0 + 6.4 \sin (3.14 \, t) + 2.1 \sin (9.42 \, t) + \ldots$

(C) $5.0 + 6.4 \cos (3.14 \, t) + 3.2 \cos (6.28 \, t) + \ldots$

(D) $5.0 + 6.4 \sin (3.14 \, t) + 3.2 \sin (6.28 \, t) + \ldots$

$$b_1 = \frac{4}{\pi} \times 5 \qquad b_2 = 0 \qquad b_3 = \frac{4}{3\pi} \times 5 \qquad b_5 = \frac{4}{5\pi} \times 5$$

**520.** The following circuit is proposed for measuring and displaying temperature. The required temperature range of the overall circuit is –100.1°C to 100.1°C with a required resolution of ±0.1°C. Analog-digital converter (ADC) resolution is defined as plus or minus one-half of a least significant bit (± 1/2 LSB).

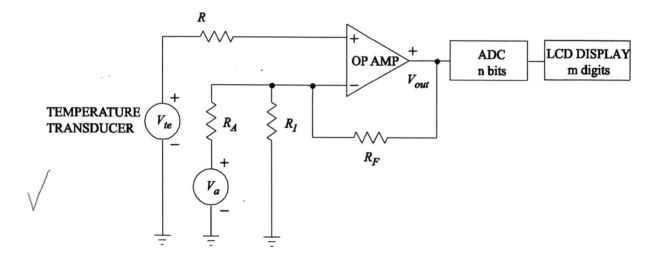

The ADC is available with resolutions of 6, 8, 10, 12 or 14 bits, not including the sign bit. Assume the ADC has only quantization error.

The **minimum** number of bits required for the ADC to achieve the specified temperature resolution is most nearly:

(A) 8

(B) 10

(C) 12

(D) 14

**521.** The logic function implemented in the circuit shown is:

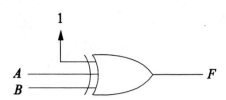

(A) $F = \overline{A}\,\overline{B} + \overline{A}B$

(B) $F = A\overline{B} + AB$

(C) $F = A\overline{B} + \overline{A}B$

(D) $F = \overline{A}\,\overline{B} + AB$

**522.** A digital system is described by $F = \Sigma(0, 1, 2, 4, 5, 7, 8, 10, 15)$ where $\Sigma$ denotes a sum of minterms. A minterm is the logical AND of a set of literals for which $F = 1$. For example, $5_{ABCD} = 0101$ represents $m_5 = \overline{A}\,B\,\overline{C}\,D$.

The minimum sum of products form for $F$ is:

(A) $F = B\,C\,D + \overline{A}\,\overline{C} + \overline{B}\,\overline{D}$

(B) $F = \overline{A}\,\overline{C} + \overline{A}\,C\,\overline{D} + A\,\overline{B}\,\overline{D} + B\,C\,D$

(C) $F = \overline{A}\,\overline{B}\,\overline{C}\,\overline{D} + \overline{A}\,\overline{B}\,\overline{C}\,D + \overline{A}\,\overline{B}\,C\,\overline{D} + \overline{A}\,B\,\overline{C}\,\overline{D} + \overline{A}\,B\,\overline{C}\,D + \overline{A}\,B\,C\,D$
$\quad + A\,\overline{B}\,\overline{C}\,\overline{D} + A\,\overline{B}\,C\,\overline{D} + A\,B\,C\,D$

(D) $F = (B + C + D)(\overline{A} + \overline{C})(\overline{B} + \overline{D})$

**523.** A motor is equipped with an optical shaft encoder to measure motor speed. The optical encoder provides 200 pulses per motor revolution. A microcontroller equipped with a real-time interrupt (RTI) capability is used to measure motor speed. The RTI interval is 32.768 ms. The microcontroller counts 372 pulses from the optical encoder in the RTI interval. The speed (rpm) of the motor is most nearly:

(A) 1

(B) 57

(C) 136

(D) 3,400

**524.** The output of a TTL NAND gate is connected to a relay as shown. The specifications for the output port of the gate and for the relay are given.

When the gate's output goes to a logic low, the relay will not activate. The designer realizes that the diode is in the circuit backwards and reverses it. However, the circuit still will not activate the relay. Which part has most likely failed?

(A) The coil of the relay has burned out.

(B) One of the gate's output transistors failed open.

(C) One of the gate's output transistors failed shorted.

(D) One of the gate's output transistors and the coil of the relay both failed.

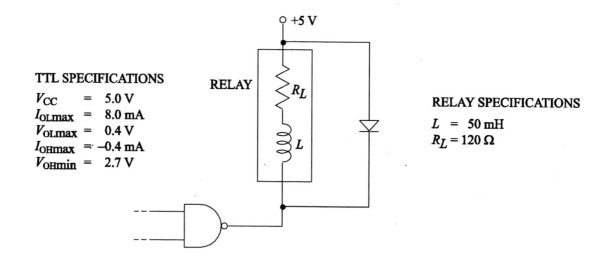

TTL SPECIFICATIONS

$V_{CC}$ = 5.0 V
$I_{OLmax}$ = 8.0 mA
$V_{OLmax}$ = 0.4 V
$I_{OHmax}$ = −0.4 mA
$V_{OHmin}$ = 2.7 V

RELAY SPECIFICATIONS

$L$ = 50 mH
$R_L$ = 120 Ω

**525.** An antenna with an effective aperture of 1 m$^2$ is connected to a receiver. In the absence of any signal, the local noise produces a received power of –40 dBm. If an incoming signal must produce a S/N of 10 dB, the RMS electric field intensity (mV/m) is most nearly:

    (A)    0.37
    (B)    1.0
    (C)    7.1
    (D)    19.5

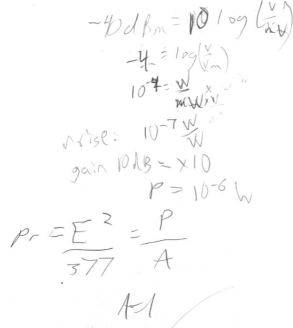

**526.** A lossy transmission line is used to connect a transmitter to an antenna. If the VSWR measured at the antenna end of the transmission line is 1.5, which of the following statements is correct?

    (A)    The VSWR measured at the transmitter end of the transmission line is smaller than 1.5.

    (B)    The VSWR measured at the transmitter end of the transmission line is larger than 1.5.

    (C)    The VSWR measured at the transmitter end of the transmission line is equal to 1.5.

    (D)    The characteristic impedance of the antenna matches exactly the characteristic impedance of the transmission line.

**527.** A quarter-wavelength long monopole protrudes out of an infinite ground plane that is a perfect electrical conductor (PEC). It is fed by a coax as shown in the figure.

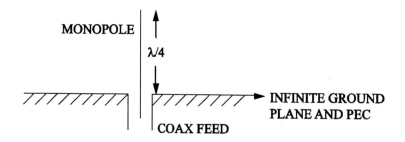

The radiation pattern for this antenna most closely resembles which of the following?

(A)

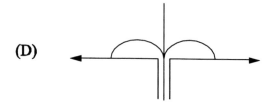

(B)

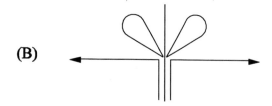

(C)

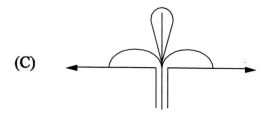

(D)

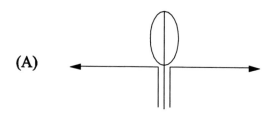

**528.** The figures below show three antenna configurations. The broader lines of the figures are the active elements of the antenna. The excitation signal of each antenna has the form shown in the figures. **Figure 1** is a single-element vertical antenna over an infinite ideal ground plane, **Figure 2** is a two-element horizontal antenna above an ideal ground plane, and **Figure 3** is a two-element horizontal antenna above an ideal ground plane with dual feed. Separation of the elements in **Figures 2** and **3** is quite small compared to the wavelength of the signal.

If the angles $|\theta_a| = |\theta_b| = |\theta_c| = 90°$, which antenna will have a dual diversity vertically and horizontally polarized radiation pattern?

(A)  **Figure 1**

(B)  **Figure 2**

(C)  **Figure 3**

(D)  None of the antennas.

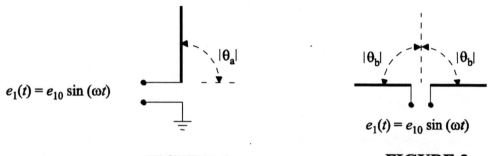

**FIGURE 1**                    **FIGURE 2**

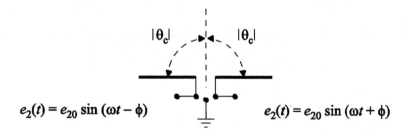

**FIGURE 3**

**529.** For the active filter shown below, $V_2$ is given by:

(A) $\left(\dfrac{R_2}{R_1 + R_2}\right)v_{in}$

(B) $-\dfrac{1}{sC_1R_3}v_{out}$

(C) $\dfrac{1}{sC_1R_3}v_{out}$

(D) $v_{in}$

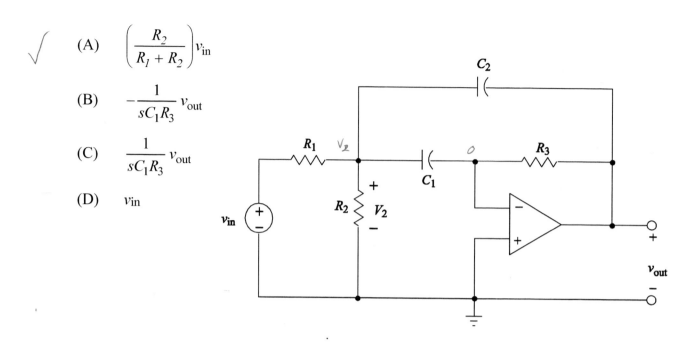

**530.** Referring to the figure, the biasing resistors $R_1$ and $R_2$ are chosen so that $V_{out}$ with no input signal is +10 Vdc. Ignore the loading effect of $R_1$ and $R_2$. When the input signal is applied, the output signal imposed on the +10 Vdc will be:

(A) a sinusoid

(B) an asymmetrical wave, sinusoidal on the positive half-cycle, flattened on the bottom

(C) an asymmetrical wave, sinusoidal on the negative half-cycle, flattened on the top

(D) a trapezoidal wave equally flattened on both cycles

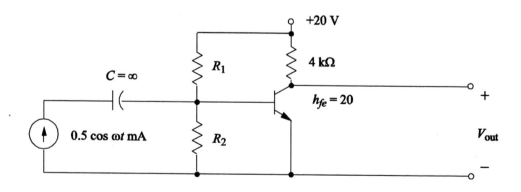

**531.** A 400-Hz quadrature phase motor driver employs two identical second-order filters with $Q$ equal to 10. The output of each filter must equal $K \sin(800\pi t + \theta)$, where $K$ is the magnitude of the input signal at 400 Hz. The transfer function of each of the filters will be most nearly:

(A) $\dfrac{(800\pi)^2}{s^2 + (80\pi)s + (800\pi)^2}$

(B) $\dfrac{s^2}{s^2 + (80\pi)s + (800\pi)^2}$

(C) $\dfrac{(80\pi)s}{s^2 + (80\pi)s + (800\pi)^2}$

(D) $\dfrac{s^2 + (800\pi)^2}{s^2 + (80\pi)s + (800\pi)^2}$

**532.** For the switching transistor shown in **Figure 1,** the base current $i_B$ has the wave shape shown in **Figure 2.** If $t_o = 2$ ms and $T = 5$ ms, the average voltage $V_{CE}$ (V) will be most nearly:

(A)   301
(B)   199
(C)   1.5
(D)   0

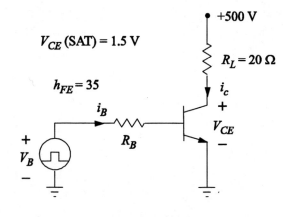

**FIGURE 1**

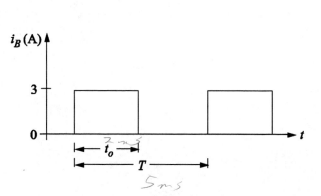

**FIGURE 2**

**533.** Referring to the figure, Q3 and Q4 are a matched pair of transistors. The collector current $I_{C3}$ is most nearly:

(A) $\dfrac{20 - V_{BE3}}{R_{C3}}$

(B) $\dfrac{20 - V_{BE3}}{(1 + 2/\beta)R_{C3}}$

(C) $\dfrac{20 - V_{BE3}}{(1 + 2\beta)R_{C3}}$

(D) $\dfrac{(20 - V_{BE3})(1 + 2/\beta)}{R_{C3}}$

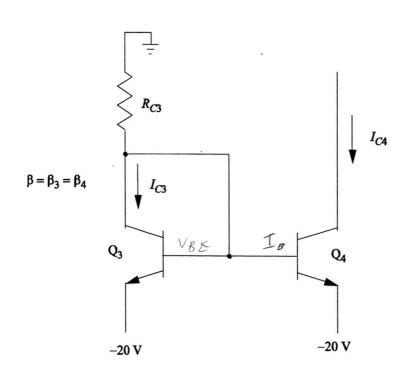

$I_{C3} + \dfrac{-20 + V_{BE}}{R_{C3}} + 2\beta I_{e3} = 0$

$I_{C3}(1 + 2\beta) = \dfrac{20 - V_{BE}}{(1 + 2\beta)R_{C3}}$

**534.** For the parameters shown in the figure, the closed-loop damping ratio is most nearly:

   (A)   0.40
   (B)   0.63
   (C)   0.70
   (D)   2.82

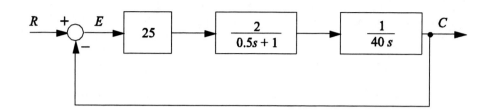

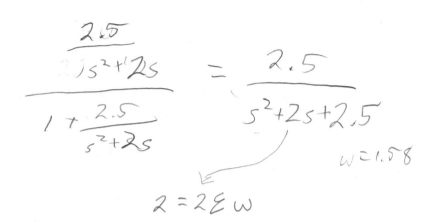

**535.** The system shown is stable for:

   (A)   $K > -2$
   (B)   $-3 < K < 0$
   (C)   $K < -2$
   (D)   $-3 < K < -2$

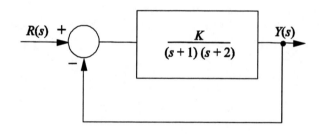

**536.** For the circuit shown, the phase shift of the transfer function $V_o/V_i$ at very high frequencies is:

(A)  90°
(B)  0°
(C)  −90°
(D)  −180°

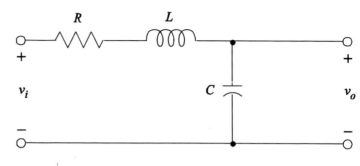

$$V_o = \frac{\frac{1}{sC}}{R+sL} = \frac{\frac{1}{C}}{s^2 L + Rs}$$

2 poles

**537.** If a carrier wave of 10 MHz is amplitude modulated by an audio signal of 1 kHz, the resultant signal to be broadcast contains only the:

(A)  10,001,000-Hz component

(B)  10,001,000-Hz and 9,999,000-Hz components

(C)  10,001,000-Hz, 10,000,000-Hz, and 9,999,000-Hz components

(D)  10,001,000-Hz, 10,000,000-Hz, 9,999,000-Hz, and 1,000-Hz components

**538.** A receiver with a noise floor of −102 dBm receives an AM signal. The total received power is −70 dBm. If the modulating signal is a square wave and the modulation index is 100%, then the signal-to-noise ratio (dB) is most nearly:

(A)  −32
(B)  29
(C)  32
(D)  35

50

**539.** A microwave relay link is used to transmit binary information and has the following specifications:

| | |
|---|---|
| Carrier frequency | 6 GHz |
| Atmospheric loss | 0.2 dB/mile |
| Transmission bandwidth | 24 MHz |
| Transmitted symbol rate | 22.368 Msymbols/sec |
| Transmitter antenna gain | 44 dB |
| Receiver antenna gain | 44 dB |
| Receiving system effective input noise temperature | 500 K |

To minimize system noise without degrading transmitted signal quality, the absolute minimum bandwidth (MHz) of the intermediate frequency (IF) filter in the receiver should be most nearly:

(A)    12.00
(B)    22.37
(C)    24.00
(D)    48.00

**540.** A digital radio system operates in a channel that exhibits the normalized multipath profile shown in the figure. The mean delay $\bar{\tau}$ (μs) for this channel is most nearly:

(A)    0.96
(B)    2.75
(C)    4
(D)    240

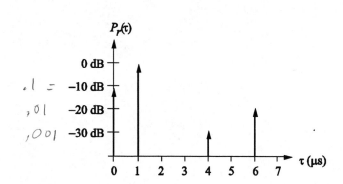

$$\frac{0 \times .1 \times 1 \times 1 + 4 \times .001 + .01 \times 6}{1 + .01 + .1 + .001}$$

This completes the afternoon session. Solutions begin on page 67.

# ELECTRICAL AND ELECTRONICS AM SOLUTIONS

# Answers to the Electrical and Electronics
## AM Practice Exam

Detailed solutions for each question begin on the next page.

| | | | |
|-----|---|-----|---|
| 101 | B | 121 | D |
| 102 | D | 122 | A |
| 103 | B | 123 | C |
| 104 | B | 124 | A |
| 105 | D | 125 | C |
| 106 | A | 126 | B |
| 107 | A | 127 | A |
| 108 | B | 128 | C |
| 109 | C | 129 | D |
| 110 | B | 130 | A |
| 111 | C | 131 | C |
| 112 | D | 132 | A |
| 113 | C | 133 | D |
| 114 | D | 134 | A |
| 115 | D | 135 | C |
| 116 | A | 136 | B |
| 117 | C | 137 | C |
| 118 | C | 138 | C |
| 119 | A | 139 | A |
| 120 | C | 140 | A |

A  12
B  7
C  13
   8

**101.**

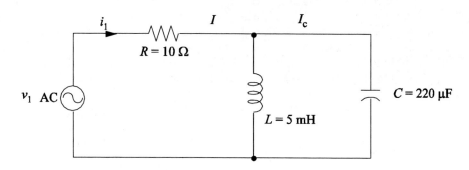

$$jωL = j(400)(5 \times 10^{-3}) = j2$$

$$-j\frac{1}{ωC} = -j\frac{1}{(400)(220 \times 10^{-6})} = -j11.364$$

$$z = 10 + \frac{(j2)(-j11.364)}{j2 - j11.364} = 10 + j2.43$$

$$I = \frac{10 \angle 0}{10 + j2.43} = 0.972 \angle -13.66$$

$$I_C = \frac{j2}{j2 - j11.364}(0.972 \angle -13.66) = -0.2076 \angle -13.66$$

$$I_{Cmax} = 0.21 \text{ A}$$

*current divider*

## THE CORRECT ANSWER IS: (B)

**102.**

$$z_{11} = z_{22} = \frac{(300)(318)}{300 + 318} = 154.37$$

$$z_{21} = z_{12} = \frac{300}{318}(300 \| 318) = 145.63$$

$$Z = \begin{bmatrix} 154.37 & 145.63 \\ 145.63 & 154.37 \end{bmatrix}$$

$$|Z| = (154.37)(154.37) - (145.63)(145.63) = 2622$$

$$y_{11} = y_{22} = \frac{z_{22}}{|Z|} = \frac{154.37}{2622} = 0.0589$$

$$y_{12} = y_{21} = \frac{-z_{12}}{|Z|} = \frac{-145.63}{2622} = -0.0555$$

$$Y = \begin{bmatrix} 0.059 & -0.056 \\ -0.056 & 0.059 \end{bmatrix} = [0.059, -0.056; -0.056, 0.059]$$

## THE CORRECT ANSWER IS: (D)

**103.** Use Norton's Theorem. The conductance will be:

$$G = \frac{(3.0 - 5.0 \times 0.2)}{5.0} = \frac{2.0}{5.0} = 0.4 \, S$$

The parallel current source will have a value of 3.0 A.

Alternate Solution:

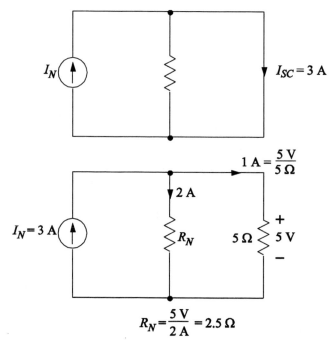

$$R_N = \frac{5 \, V}{2 \, A} = 2.5 \, \Omega$$

**THE CORRECT ANSWER IS: (B)**


**104.** $I_A = 5/2 = 2.5 \, A$

$G_B = 1/R_B = 0.25 \, S$

**THE CORRECT ANSWER IS: (B)**


**105.** At $t = 0$,

$$v(0) = 6\left(\frac{2k}{3k}\right) = 4 \, V$$

Given $R = 2 \, k\Omega$, $C = 3 \times 10^{-6} \, F$, thus $\tau = RC = 2{,}000 \times 3 \times 10^{-6} = 6 \, ms$

$v(0) = A + B = 4$

$v(\infty) = A = 0$

Therefore, $B = 4$

**THE CORRECT ANSWER IS: (D)**

**106.** $R = V/I$ at the peak. $R = 169$ V/5 A = 33.8 $\Omega$.

**THE CORRECT ANSWER IS: (A)**

**107.** Since the frequencies of the two components of the current are different, the total power may be calculated as:

$$P = \left(\frac{5}{\sqrt{2}}\right)^2 (3) + \left(\frac{2}{\sqrt{2}}\right)^2 (3)$$

$$= \left(\frac{25}{2}\right)(3) + \left(\frac{4}{2}\right)(3)$$

$$= 43.5 \text{ W} \cong 44 \text{ W}$$

**THE CORRECT ANSWER IS: (A)**

**108.** First calculate the magnitude of the voltage:

$$V = \frac{50\angle 45°}{\sqrt{2}} + \frac{28.28\angle 0°}{\sqrt{2}}$$

$$= \left(\frac{50}{\sqrt{2}}\right)(0.707 + j0.707) + 20$$

$$= 25 + j25 + 20$$

$$= 45 + j25$$

$$= 51.5\angle 29° \text{ V}$$

The rms value of the voltage is 51.5 V. The power is computed by:

$$P = \frac{V^2}{R} = \frac{(51.5)^2}{5} = 530 \text{ W}$$

**THE CORRECT ANSWER IS: (B)**

**109.** Note that the voltage drop across the series regulator is 14 − 5 = 9 V. The current passing through the series regulator is 5/5 = 1 A, making the total power dissipation in the regulator (9)(1) = 9 W. The case temperature derating curve has the form $P_{Dmax} = 15 - 0.25T$, where $T$ is the free air temperature. Solving for $T$ given a power dissipation of 9 W gives a maximum operating temperature of 114°C.

**THE CORRECT ANSWER IS: (C)**

**110.** Two capacitors in series (parallel) combine like two resistors in parallel (series).

$$C_{AB} = \frac{1}{\frac{1}{30} + \frac{1}{30}} = \frac{30}{2} = 15\ \mu F$$

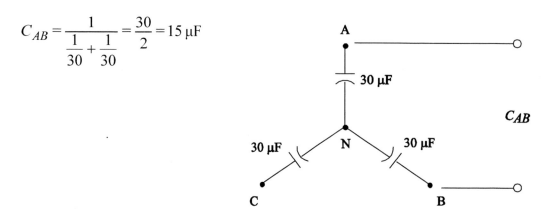

**THE CORRECT ANSWER IS: (B)**

**111.** $V_o = -\dfrac{R_2}{R_1 + R_s} V_s$

$$V_o\big|_{max} = -\frac{R_2(max)}{R_1 + R_s}(-100\ mV)$$

$$= -\frac{(1.01)10^6}{10 \times 10^3}\left(-100 \times 10^{-3}\right)$$

$$= 10.1\ V$$

**THE CORRECT ANSWER IS: (C)**

**112.** The coefficients, $b_i$, are linear in all cases except (D).

**THE CORRECT ANSWER IS: (D)**

**113.**

$$V_p = \frac{R_2}{R_1 + R_2} V_1$$

$$V_n = V_p$$

$$0 = \frac{V_n - V_2}{R_3} + \frac{V_n - V_{out}}{R_4}$$

$$V_{out} = \left(1 + \frac{R_4}{R_3}\right) V_n - \frac{R_4}{R_3} V_2$$

$$= \left(\frac{R_2}{R_1 + R_2}\right)\left(1 + \frac{R_4}{R_3}\right) V_1 - \frac{R_4}{R_3} V_2$$

$$V_{out} = K(V_1 - V_2)$$

$$\left(\frac{R_2}{R_1 + R_2}\right)\left(1 + \frac{R_4}{R_3}\right) = \frac{R_4}{R_3}$$

$$\frac{R_3}{R_4}\left(1 + \frac{R_4}{R_3}\right) = \frac{R_1 + R_2}{R_2}$$

$$\left(\frac{R_3}{R_4} + 1\right) = \left(\frac{R_1}{R_2} + 1\right)$$

$$\frac{R_3}{R_4} = \frac{R_1}{R_2}$$

**THE CORRECT ANSWER IS: (C)**


**114.** The circuit transfer function (with $s = j\omega$), has a magnitude of

$$|G(\omega)| = \left|\frac{\frac{1}{j\omega C}}{R}\right| = \left|\frac{1}{RCj\omega}\right| = \frac{1}{RC\omega}$$

This is a straight line in Bode plot terms, with the magnitude decreasing based on the frequency $\omega$. [Note $s = j\omega = j(2\pi f)$]. The 0 dB point (unity gain) occurs when $\omega = \omega_c = 1/RC$. These characteristics are present in (D).

**THE CORRECT ANSWER IS: (D)**

**115.** $P_1 = (1 - R_1) = (1 - 0.92) = 0.08$

$P_2 = (1 - R_2) = (1 - 0.85) = 0.15$

$R_1 \| R_2 = 1 - (P_1 \times P_2)$

$\qquad = 1 - (0.08)(0.15)$

$\qquad = 1 - 0.012$

$\qquad = 0.988$

**THE CORRECT ANSWER IS: (D)**

**116.** $f_s$ = sampling frequency

$f_m$ = maximum signal frequency

$f_m \leq 1/2\, f_s$

**THE CORRECT ANSWER IS: (A)**

**117.** $\dfrac{1}{z^{-1}(1 - 0.7z^{-1})} = \dfrac{z}{(z - 0.7)/z} = \dfrac{z^2}{z - 0.7} \Rightarrow$ pole at $z = 0.7$

**THE CORRECT ANSWER IS: (C)**

**118.** The step size is 10 V/16 = 0.625 V. Since the encoding of the A/D converter is offset by –5 V, the true voltage magnitude being encoded is 2 V – (–5 V) = 7 V. 7 V/0.625 V = 11.2, which is $(1011)_2$.

**THE CORRECT ANSWER IS: (C)**

**119.** The initial value theorem for the Laplace transform states that

$$f(t) \big|_{t=0} = \lim_{s \to \infty} s[F(s)]$$

so $\qquad f(t) \big|_{t=0} = \lim_{s \to \infty} \dfrac{s\,(s + 6)}{s\,(s + 2)(s + 3)}$

$$= \lim_{s \to \infty} \dfrac{(s + 6)}{s^2 + 5s + 6}$$

$$= \lim_{s \to \infty} \dfrac{1}{2s + 5} \qquad \text{by L'Hospitals Rule}$$

$$\dfrac{1}{\infty} = 0$$

**THE CORRECT ANSWER IS: (A)**

**120.** Aliasing has occurred. A 70-Hz signal sampled at 128 Hz will alias down to 58 Hz.

**THE CORRECT ANSWER IS: (C)**

**121.** Simple conversion from POS to SOP, can be accomplished in any number of ways. Here is one of them:

$$(\overline{A} + B)(\overline{B} + \overline{C})(A + C) = (\overline{A}\,\overline{B} + \overline{A}\,\overline{C} + B\overline{B} + B\overline{C})(A + C)$$
$$= (\overline{A}\,\overline{B}A + \overline{A}\,\overline{B}C + \overline{A}\,\overline{C}A + \overline{A}\,\overline{C}C + B\overline{C}A + B\overline{C}C)$$
$$= \overline{A}\,\overline{B}C + AB\overline{C}$$

**THE CORRECT ANSWER IS: (D)**

**122.** Two AND gates into an OR gate yields $AB + CB = B(A + C)$.

**THE CORRECT ANSWER IS: (A)**

**123.** If any input is high, the input voltage to the last inverter is low, making F high and resulting in an OR.

**THE CORRECT ANSWER IS: (C)**

**124.** The bit format for the floating point number is as follows:

$$S=(0)_2 \; E=(1000000)_2 \; M=(00000000)_2.$$

The sign bit S is 0, indicating a positive number. The exponent field has value 64, when converted from excess-64 yields 0 as the true exponent value. The mantissa is zero, so the data value is:

$$0 \times 2^0 = 0.0, \text{ or value} = -1^S (M * 2^{E-64}) = (+1)(0.0 * 2^{64-64}) = 0.0$$

**THE CORRECT ANSWER IS: (A)**

**125.** $H = \dfrac{I}{2\pi R} = \dfrac{50}{0.2\pi} = 79.6 \text{ A/m}$

**THE CORRECT ANSWER IS: (C)**

**126.** The actual velocity is:

$$v_p = \frac{2L}{\tau_0}$$

The ratio of the actual velocity to the velocity of the light is therefore:

$$\frac{v_p}{v_c} = \frac{2L}{\tau_0 v_c}$$

where: $L = 1{,}000$ M

$\tau_0 = 9.43$ μs

$v_c = 3 \times 10^8$ M/s

The ratio is therefore equal to 0.70696.

**THE CORRECT ANSWER IS: (B)**

**127.** The current distribution in (A) results in a radiation pattern with two main lobes. The remaining distributions have radiation patterns with many more lobes.

**THE CORRECT ANSWER IS: (A)**

**128.** The answer can be determined with a Smith chart by finding the length of shorted stub that gives $-j\dfrac{0.04}{0.01333}$ $= -3$

where 0.04 is the desired susceptance and 0.01333 is the $Y_0$ for the 75-Ω line.

Analytically, the input $Z_0$ for the shorted stub $Z_{in} = Z_0 \, (-j) \tan \dfrac{2\pi l}{\lambda} = \dfrac{1}{-j0.04} = j\,25$

so $\tan \dfrac{2\pi l}{\lambda} = \dfrac{25}{75} = \dfrac{1}{3}$ $\qquad \dfrac{360°l}{\lambda} = 18.43°$

$\dfrac{l}{\lambda} = \dfrac{18.43}{360} = 0.05119$

$l = 0.05119\,(80 \text{ cm})$

$= 4.09 \text{ cm} = 40.9 \text{ mm}$

**THE CORRECT ANSWER IS: (C)**

**129.** $V_{gs} = V_{in}$

$$0 = \frac{V_{out} - V_{in}}{R_G} + g_m V_{in} + \frac{V_{out}}{R_D} + \frac{V_{out}}{R_L}$$

$$\left(\frac{1}{R_G} - g_m\right)V_{in} = \left(\frac{1}{R_G} + \frac{1}{R_D} + \frac{1}{R_L}\right)V_{out}$$

$$\frac{V_{out}}{V_{in}} = \frac{\dfrac{1}{R_G} - g_m}{\dfrac{1}{R_G} + \dfrac{1}{R_D} + \dfrac{1}{R_L}} = \frac{1 - g_m R_G}{1 + \dfrac{R_G}{R_D} + \dfrac{R_G}{R_L}}$$

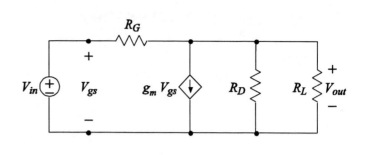

**THE CORRECT ANSWER IS: (D)**

**130.** General form of band-pass filter is

$$\frac{a_1 s}{s^2 + \left(\dfrac{\omega_o}{Q}\right)s + (\omega_o)^2}$$

where $\omega_o$ = center frequency

$$BW = \frac{\omega_o}{Q} = \text{3-db bandwidth}$$

$10^5$ rad/s

**THE CORRECT ANSWER IS: (A)**

**131.** $V_i = 4$ V, $R_i = 2$ kΩ, $R_c = 1$ kΩ
$V_+ = V_- = V_i$ and $I_+ = I_- = 0$

Then $I_c = \dfrac{V_i}{R_c} = \dfrac{4}{1k} = 4$ mA

$V_o = V_c + V_- = 2 + 4 = 6$ V

**THE CORRECT ANSWER IS: (C)**

**132.** In the two-inverter circuit the total loop phase shift must be 360° in order to sustain oscillation. At the series-resonant frequency $f_s$, the impedance of the crystal is only resistance, so series resonance must be used.

**THE CORRECT ANSWER IS: (A)**

**133.** $I_Z = K[V_{GS2} - V_T]^2$

$$V_{GS2} = \sqrt{\frac{I_Z}{K}} + V_T = 1.4472 \text{ V}$$

$$V_{S2} = V_X - V_{GS2} = 3.553 \text{ V}$$

$$R = \frac{V_{S2}}{I_Z} = 355 \text{ k}\Omega$$

**THE CORRECT ANSWER IS: (D)**

**134.** $\dfrac{Y}{R} = G_4 + \dfrac{G_1 G_2}{1 + G_2 H_2}$

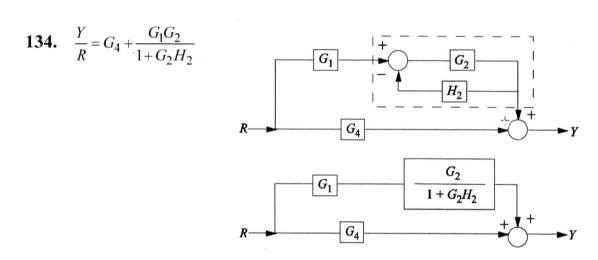

**THE CORRECT ANSWER IS: (A)**

**135.** Collapsing the feedback loop yields the following transfer function:

$$\frac{Y(s)}{U(s)} = \frac{\dfrac{1}{s^2 + 3s + 4}}{\left[1 + \dfrac{2}{s^2 + 3s + 4}\right]}(s + 4) = \frac{s + 4}{s^2 + 3s + 6}$$

Breaking this into two functions, $\dfrac{X(s)}{U(s)} \dfrac{Y(s)}{X(s)}$, yields:

$$\frac{X(s)}{U(s)} = \frac{1}{s^2 + 3s + 6} \quad \text{and} \quad \frac{Y(s)}{X(s)} = s + 4$$

This yields the following differential equations:

$$\ddot{x} = u - 3\dot{x} - 6x \quad \text{and} \quad y = \dot{x} + 4x$$

Substituting $x(t) = x_1(t)$ and $dx(t)/dt = x_2(t)$.

$$\begin{bmatrix} \dot{x}_1 \\ \dot{x}_2 \end{bmatrix} = \begin{bmatrix} 0 & 1 \\ -6 & -3 \end{bmatrix} \begin{bmatrix} x_1 \\ x_2 \end{bmatrix} + \begin{bmatrix} 0 \\ 1 \end{bmatrix} u \quad \text{and} \quad y = \begin{bmatrix} 4 & 1 \end{bmatrix} \begin{bmatrix} x_1 \\ x_2 \end{bmatrix}$$

**THE CORRECT ANSWER IS: (C)**

**136.** The initial slope of the magnitude plot is –20 db/dec, and the initial phase shift of the phase plot is –90°. Either of these facts requires that there be a pole at the origin. That is, there is a $1/s$ term in the open-loop transfer function.

The final slope of the magnitude plot is –60 db/dec, and the final phase shift of the phase plot is –270°. Either of these facts requires that the pole-zero excess be three. This requires at least two poles other than the one at the origin.

In addition, the response has a resonance peak at the breakpoint at 100 Hz. This requires a complex pole pair.

**THE CORRECT ANSWER IS: (B)**

**137.** $x(t) = 40 \cos (200,000 \, \pi t) \quad + \quad 10 \cos (197,000 \, \pi t) \quad + \quad 10 \cos (203,000 \, \pi t)$

carrier term           lower side band(LSB)     upper side band (USB)

$x_{AM}(t) = A_C \, [1 + m \cos (\omega_{msg} t)] \, \cos (\omega_C t)$

where:   $A_C$ = carrier amplitude
            m = modulation index
            $\omega_{msg}$ = message frequency
            $\omega_C$ = carrier frequency

Comparing $x(t)$ to $x_{AM}(t)$ results in $A_C = 40$ and $\omega_C = 200,000\pi$

Since $x_{AM}(t) = A_C \cos \omega_C(t) + A_C m \cos (\omega_{msg} t) \cos (\omega_C t)$

then using $2 \cos \alpha \cos \beta = \cos (\alpha - \beta) + \cos (\alpha + \beta)$

$x_{AM}(t) = 40 \cos(\omega_C t) + 40 \, m \cos(\omega_{msg} t) \cos (\omega_C t)$

$\qquad = 40 \cos(\omega_C t) + 10 \cos(197,000 \, \pi t) + 10 \cos(203,000 \, \pi t)$

$\omega_{msg} = 3000 \, \pi t$ and

$10 \cos (197,000 \, \pi t) + 10 \cos (203,000 \, \pi t) = 20 \cos (3000 \, \pi t) \cos (200,000 \, \pi t)$

which is also equal to $40 \, m \cos (3000 \, \pi t) \cos (200,000 \, \pi t)$

so, m = 0.5

$0.5 \times 100\% = 50\%$

% modulation is 50%

**THE CORRECT ANSWER IS: (C)**

**138.**  $F_1 = 5$ dB $= 3.16$      $F_2 = 15$ dB $= 31.62$      $F_3 = 25$ dB $= 316.23$
$G_1 = 10$ dB $= 10$      $G_2 = 15$ dB $= 31.62$      $G_3 = 20$ dB $= 100$

$$F_T = F_1 + \frac{F_2 - 1}{G_1} + \frac{F_3 - 1}{G_1 G_2} = 7.221 = 8.586 \text{ dB}$$

**THE CORRECT ANSWER IS: (C)**


**139.**  ATM provides connection-oriented service with both permanent and switched virtual circuits.

**THE CORRECT ANSWER IS: (A)**


**140.**  Free space loss $= 20 \log \left[ \dfrac{4 \pi d}{c/f} \right]$

$d = 8$ miles $= 12{,}874.752$ m
$f = 23.6 \times 10^9$ Hz
$c = 3 \times 10^8$ m/sec

Free space loss $= 141.98$ dB

**THE CORRECT ANSWER IS: (A)**

# ELECTRICAL AND ELECTRONICS PM SOLUTIONS

# Answers to the Electrical and Electronics
## PM Practice Exam

Detailed solutions for each question begin on the next page.

| | | | |
|---|---|---|---|
| 501 | B | 521 | D |
| 502 | A | 522 | A |
| 503 | A | 523 | D |
| 504 | C | 524 | B |
| 505 | A | 525 | D |
| 506 | C | 526 | A |
| 507 | B | 527 | D |
| 508 | B | 528 | C |
| 509 | D | 529 | B |
| 510 | B | 530 | D |
| 511 | C | 531 | C |
| 512 | B | 532 | A |
| 513 | B | 533 | B |
| 514 | D | 534 | B |
| 515 | B | 535 | A |
| 516 | A | 536 | D |
| 517 | D | 537 | C |
| 518 | B | 538 | B |
| 519 | B | 539 | C |
| 520 | B | 540 | A |

**501.** $\omega = 2\pi f = 2\pi(160) = 1005$ rad/s

$X_L = j\omega L = j(1005)(0.2) = j\,201\,\Omega$

$X_C = -j\dfrac{1}{\omega C} = -j\dfrac{1}{(1005)(4\times10^{-6})}$

$X_C = -j\,249\,\Omega$

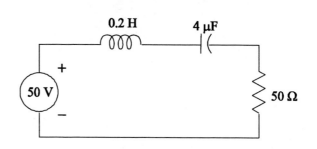

By voltage division :

$V_R = \dfrac{50}{50 + j\,201 - j\,249}\,(50\angle 0°)$

$V_R = 36.07\angle 43.8°$   rms

$\therefore V_{peak} = V_{R_{rms}}\left(\dfrac{1}{0.707}\right)$

$V_{peak} = 51$ V

**THE CORRECT ANSWER IS: (B)**

**502.** The inductor will change its voltage to keep the current flow at $t = 0_+$ the same as the current at $t = 0_-$.

At $t = 0_-$      $I_L = \dfrac{12\text{ V}}{24.2\,\Omega} = 0.496$ A

At $t = 0_+$      $I_L = 0.496$ A  and this flows in the 10-k$\Omega$ resistor.

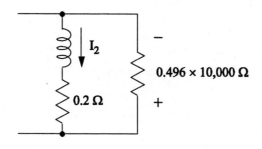

$v \cong -5,000$ V as originally shown

**THE CORRECT ANSWER IS: (A)**

**503.**

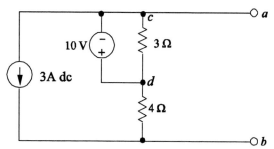

Open circuit: The voltage across the 3-$\Omega$ resistor is constrained by the voltage source to be 10 V.

Open circuit: The 3A can only flow through the 4-$\Omega$ resistor so producing 12 V.

Open circuit $V_{ba} = 10 + 12 = 22$ V $= V_{ba}$ with $b$ most positive so $V_{ab} = -22$ V

Suppressing the sources, the 10 V is a short. The 3A is an open, so $R_T = 4\ \Omega$.

The correct answer is (A).

Alternate Solution by Superposition:

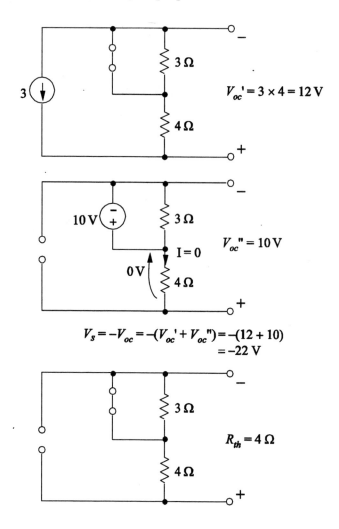

$$V_{oc}' = 3 \times 4 = 12\,\text{V}$$

$$V_{oc}'' = 10\,\text{V}$$

$$V_s = -V_{oc} = -(V_{oc}' + V_{oc}'') = -(12 + 10)$$
$$= -22\,\text{V}$$

$$R_{th} = 4\,\Omega$$

**THE CORRECT ANSWER IS: (A)**

**504.** Opening $i_g$, the voltage across it is $\frac{6}{9} \times 10$ V by the voltage divider equation.

Suppressing $V_g$

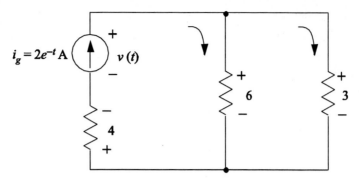

The voltage across the generator is $(4\ \Omega + 2\ \Omega) \times 2\ e^{-t} = 12\ e^{-t}$ V.
Both voltages are positive as shown.

So by superposition:

$$v(t) = \frac{60}{9} + \frac{12 \times 9}{9} e^{-t}$$

$$v(t) = \frac{60 + 108\ e^{-t}}{9}\ \text{V}$$

**THE CORRECT ANSWER IS: (C)**

**505.** Since the average of a sine wave is zero, the dc voltage across the 0.022 µF capacitor is $\frac{1}{3} \times 5$ V by the voltage divider equation = 1.666 V

**THE CORRECT ANSWER IS: (A)**

**506.** Maximum power occurs when $Z_L$ is a conjugate match for $Z_{source}$.

$$Z_{source} = 600 + j\ 2\ \pi \times 10^6 \times 50 \times 10^{-6}$$
$$= 600 + j\ 314,\ \text{so optimum}\ Z_L = 600 - j\ 314$$

The reactance of $Z_L$ is capacitive

$$\frac{1}{2\pi \times 10^6 \times C_L} = 314$$
$$C_L = 507\ \text{pF}$$

**THE CORRECT ANSWER IS: (C)**

**507.** $T_A + P\theta_{jA} = Tj$

$30 + 4\,\theta_{jA} = 150°C$

$\theta_{jA} = \dfrac{120}{4} = 30°C/W$

so if $P = 1.5\ W$ and $T_A = 30$

$30° + 30°C/W \times 1.5\ W = 75°C$

Alternate Solution:

Thermal resistance $= \dfrac{150 - 30}{4\ W} = 30°C/W$

Junction temperature $= T_{ambient} + $ thermal resistance $\cdot$ power

$= 30°C + (30°C/W)(1.5\ W)$

$= 75°C$

**THE CORRECT ANSWER IS: (B)**


**508.** Minimum current occurs when $\left|X_L\right| = \left|X_C\right|$

at $f = \dfrac{100}{2\pi}$ Hz, $\qquad \omega L = 20 \times 100$

$= 2{,}000\ \Omega$

$X_C = \dfrac{1}{100\ C} = 2{,}000$

$\dfrac{1}{C} = 200{,}000$

$C = 5 \times 10^{-6}\ F$

$\dfrac{1}{\omega C} = \omega L$

**THE CORRECT ANSWER IS: (B)**


**509.** $k\sqrt{L_1 L_2} = $ mutual inductance

$M = 0.75\,(4) = 3\ H$

Total inductance is

$L_1 + L_2 + 2M = 8 + 6 = 14\ H$

**THE CORRECT ANSWER IS: (D)**

**510.** $V_C = 20(1 - e^{-t/RC})$

$V_C = 10$ when $e^{-t/RC} = 0.5$

$-\dfrac{t}{RC} = -0.693$

$RC = \dfrac{1}{0.693} = 1.44$ sec

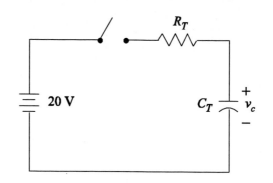

If $C = 1$ farad

$R_{TOTAL} = 1.44\ \Omega$

$R_{TOTAL} = 0.5 + R_X$

$R_X = 0.9\ \Omega$

**THE CORRECT ANSWER IS: (B)**

**511.** $f_{max} = 10$ Hz $\qquad V_{peak} = 5$ V

$V_{in} = 5\cos 62.8\,t$

$\dfrac{dV}{dt} = 314 \sin 62.8\,t$

$\left.\dfrac{dV}{dt}\right|_{max} = \left.\dfrac{dV}{dt}\right|_{t=0} = 314 \sin 62.8\,t\big|_{t=0}$

$\left.\dfrac{dV}{dt}\right|_{max} = 314$

$\Delta V_{max} = \left.\dfrac{dV}{dt}\right|_{max} \times 0.01$

$\Delta V_{max} = (314)(0.01) = 3.14$ V

**THE CORRECT ANSWER IS: (C)**

**512.** Gain is $\dfrac{-Z_f}{Z_i} = \dfrac{j80k}{20k} = j4$ or $4\angle 90°$

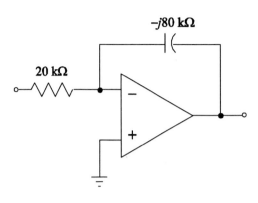

**THE CORRECT ANSWER IS: (B)**

**513.**

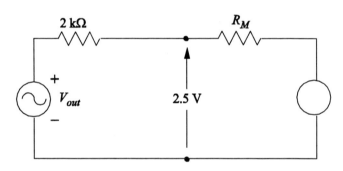

$R_M = 2,000\ \Omega/\text{V} \times 5\ V_{fs} = 10,000\ \Omega$

$2.5 = V_{out}\dfrac{10,000}{12,000}$

$V_{out} = 3\ \text{V}$

New meter

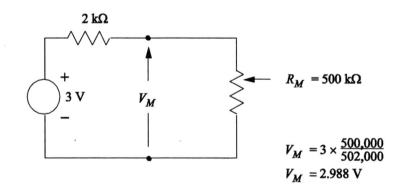

$R_M = 500\ \text{k}\Omega$

$V_M = 3 \times \dfrac{500,000}{502,000}$

$V_M = 2.988\ \text{V}$

**THE CORRECT ANSWER IS: (B)**

**514.** Since $I_{\text{sense}} = 0\ \mu\text{A}$, the resistances of leads B and C have no effect. Since $I = 10\ \text{mA}$ is a current source, leads A and D have no effect. Therefore, any error is due to $I$.

**THE CORRECT ANSWER IS: (D)**

**515.** $Z_p = 3^2 \times Z_s = 9 \times 15 = 135\ \Omega$

$I_p = \left( \dfrac{90}{90 + 135} \right)(187.5 \times 10^{-3}) = 75\ \text{mA}$

The current through the 90-$\Omega$ resistor is $(187.5 - 75)\ \text{mA} = 112.5\ \text{mA}$

$V_p = (112.5\ \text{mA})(90\ \Omega) = 10.125\ \text{V}$

$VA = V_p \times I_p = (10.125\ \text{V})(75\ \text{mA}) = 0.7594\ \text{VA}$

**THE CORRECT ANSWER IS: (B)**

**516.** The channel capacity $C = B\ \log_2[1 + \dfrac{S}{N}]$.

where $B$ is the desired bandwidth, and $S/N$ is the signal-to-noise ratio.

$400\ \text{k} = B \log_2[1 + 31.622]$

Evaluate $\log_2[1 + 31.622]$

$2^y = 32.622$

$y \ln 2 = \ln 32.622$

$y = 5.0277$

so $B = \dfrac{400\ \text{k}}{5.0277} = 79.55\ \text{kHz}$

**THE CORRECT ANSWER IS: (A)**

**517.** Transport delays are detrimental to stability because they provide no attenuation and produce a phase lag that increases linearly with frequency.

**THE CORRECT ANSWER IS: (D)**

**518.** The square wave shown has a total period of 4 milliseconds/cycle,

$$\text{so } f = \frac{1}{4 \times 10^{-3}} = 250 \text{ Hz}$$

The third harmonic is $3 \times 250 = 750$ Hz

**THE CORRECT ANSWER IS: (B)**

**519.** First, recognize that the average (or dc) value of this signal is 5.0, which appears in all four options. If this average value is subtracted from the given signal, the resulting signal has both odd symmetry and half-wave symmetry. For odd symmetry, only sine terms are present. For half-wave symmetry, each half cycle is an inverted version of the adjacent half-cycle, and only odd-harmonic terms are present. Only option (B) meets both of these conditions and is the correct answer with the correct coefficients and harmonics.

**THE CORRECT ANSWER IS: (B)**

**520.** The range required, 200.2°C with the resolution of 0.1°C requires 2,002 steps.

$$2^{11} = 2,048$$

The error specified, $\pm 0.1$°C, means that 1 bit less may be used.

**THE CORRECT ANSWER IS: (B)**

**521.** The circuit is an exclusive OR gate. Since it has three inputs, it will produce its output with any one of the three inputs **or** all three inputs. Since one input is high, output is limited to $\overline{A}\,\overline{B}$ or $AB$ for the "all three" case. The exclusive OR gate produces a "1" out if there is an odd number of 1's in.

$$\overline{A}\,\overline{B} + AB$$

Alternate Solution:

The truth table

| $A$ | $B$ | $C = 1$ | $A \oplus B$ | $F = A \oplus B \oplus C$ |
|---|---|---|---|---|
| 0 | 0 | 1 | 0 | 1 |
| 0 | 1 | 1 | 1 | 0 |
| 1 | 0 | 1 | 1 | 0 |
| 1 | 1 | 1 | 0 | 1 |

By inspection, $F = \overline{A}\,\overline{B} + AB$

**THE CORRECT ANSWER IS: (D)**

**522.** $F = \Sigma\ 0, 1, 2, 4, 5, 7, 8, 10, 15$

| CD\AB | 00 | 01 | 11 | 10 |
|-------|----|----|----|----|
| 00    | 1  | 1  | 0  | 1  |
| 01    | 1  | 1  | 0  | 0  |
| 11    | 0  | 1  | 1  | 0  |
| 10    | 1  | 0  | 0  | 1  |

$$F = \overline{A}\overline{C} + \overline{B}\overline{D} + BCD$$

**THE CORRECT ANSWER IS: (A)**

**523.** Motor speed (rpm) $= \left(\dfrac{372 \text{ pulses}}{32.768 \text{ ms}}\right)\left(\dfrac{1 \text{ revolution}}{200 \text{ pulses}}\right)\left(\dfrac{1,000 \text{ ms}}{\text{s}}\right)\left(\dfrac{60 \text{ s}}{\text{min}}\right) = 3,400 \text{ rpm}$

**THE CORRECT ANSWER IS: (D)**

**524.** The diode conducts, effectively shorting the gate's output to the power supply. This result assumes the snubber diode has been chosen large enough to absorb the relay's energy if it has been installed correctly. Hence the output transistor of the gate is the first to go.

**THE CORRECT ANSWER IS: (B)**

**525.** $A_c = 1 \text{ m}^2$

$P_R = -40 \text{ dBm} + 10 \text{ dB} = -30 \text{ dBm}$

$P_R \text{ (dBm)} = 10 \log_{10}\left[\dfrac{P_R \text{ (W)}}{\text{MW}}\right]$

$P_R = 10^{-6} \text{ W}$

$\dfrac{E_{\text{rms}}^2}{377\ \Omega} = \dfrac{P_R}{A_c} = 10^{-6} \text{ W/m}^2$

$E_{\text{rms}} = \sqrt{(377)(10^{-6})} = 0.0194 \text{ V/m}$

$= 19.4 \text{ mV/m}$

**THE CORRECT ANSWER IS: (D)**

**526.** The line loss reduces the magnitude of the reflected wave. Option (D) is only possible with infinite loss.

**THE CORRECT ANSWER IS: (A)**

**527.** Since the antenna is $\lambda/4$, there are no multiple lobes, eliminating Options (B) and (C), and there will be no radiation off the end, so the answer is Option (D).

If the ground plane is a PEC, the electric field lines terminate on it.

**THE CORRECT ANSWER IS: (D)**

**528.** The only antenna in the figures that has dual diversity is **Figure 3** since it has two radiating elements separated by a small distance with the antenna's voltage having a small phase difference. The radiation pattern will be both vertically and horizontally polarized.

**THE CORRECT ANSWER IS: (C)**

**529.** The contents of the dotted box are a differentiator where

$$\frac{v_0}{v_1} = -\frac{Z_f}{Z_{in}}$$

$$\therefore \quad v_0(s) = \frac{-R_3}{\frac{1}{s\,C_1}} v_1(s)$$

so

$$v_1(s) = -v_0(s)\frac{1}{s\,C_1 R_3}$$

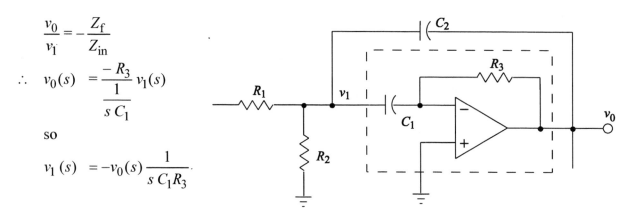

**THE CORRECT ANSWER IS: (B)**

**530.** The collector current will be $h_{fe} = 20$ times the input current of $0.5 \cos \omega t$ mA or $-10 \cos \omega t$ mA since $(10 \text{ mA}) \times (4 \text{ k}\Omega) = 40$ V. $10$ V $\pm 40$ V will clip top and bottom. The output current and voltage will be flattened at both positive and negative excursions.

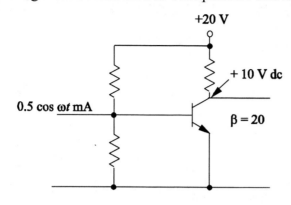

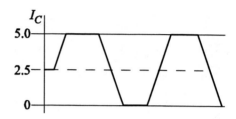

$I_C = (10 \text{ V})/(4 \text{ k}\Omega) = 2.5$ mA

**THE CORRECT ANSWER IS: (D)**

**531.** At $s = j\,800\,\pi$ only C gives an output of 1

At $s = j\,800\,\pi$:

$$\frac{(80\,\pi)(j\,800\,\pi)}{(j\,800\,\pi)^2 + (80\,\pi)(j\,800\,\pi) + (800\,\pi)^2} = \frac{80\,\pi(j\,800\,\pi)}{80\,\pi(j\,800\,\pi)} = 1$$

**THE CORRECT ANSWER IS: (C)**

**532.** $I_B = 3$ A on peaks
$I_C = h_{fe}\,I_B = 105$ A but $105$ A $\times 20\,\Omega = 2{,}100$ V
so the transistor saturates.

The collector voltage is 1.5 V for 2 ms, and 500 V for 3 ms.

$$V_{avg} = \frac{1}{5}(1.5 \times 2 + 500 \times 3) = 300.6 \text{ V}$$

**THE CORRECT ANSWER IS: (A)**

**533.** $I_{B3} = I_{B4} = \dfrac{I_{C3}}{\beta}$

Total current through $R_{C3}$ is $I_{C3} + I_{B3} + I_{B4} = I_{C3} + \dfrac{I_{C3}}{\beta} + \dfrac{I_{C3}}{\beta} = \dfrac{20 - V_{BE3}}{R_{C3}}$

$I_{C3}(1 + 2/\beta) = \dfrac{20 - V_{BE3}}{R_{C3}}$

$\therefore \quad I_{C3} = \dfrac{20 - V_{BE3}}{(1 + 2/\beta)R_{C3}}$

**THE CORRECT ANSWER IS: (B)**

**534.** Open-loop transfer function $= 50/[40s(0.5s + 1)]$
Closed-loop transfer function $= 2.5/(s^2 + 2s + 2.5)$
$\omega_n = 1.58$
$2\xi\omega_n = 2$
$\xi = 1/\omega_n = 0.633$

**THE CORRECT ANSWER IS: (B)**

**535.** $\dfrac{C}{R} = \dfrac{G}{1 + G} = \dfrac{N(s)}{D(s)}$

$D(s) = (s + 1)(s + 2) + K$
$\quad\quad = s^2 + 3s + (2 + K)$

Therefore the system is stable only for $K > -2$

**THE CORRECT ANSWER IS: (A)**

**536.** $\dfrac{V_o}{V_i} = \dfrac{1/SC}{R + SL + 1/SC} = \dfrac{1}{RCS + LCS^2 + 1}$

The pole zero excess is 2, and each pole contributes $-90°$ to the high frequency phase shift $\Rightarrow$ $-180°$

**THE CORRECT ANSWER IS: (D)**

**537.** An amplitude (AM) signal contains both carrier and upper and lower sidebands.

**THE CORRECT ANSWER IS: (C)**

**538.** Amplitude modulation reduces the power by 1/2 which is 3 dB. The difference between noise floor and total received power is 32. Thus, the signal-to-noise ratio is 29.

**THE CORRECT ANSWER IS: (B)**

**539.** The intermediate frequency (IF) filter is a band-pass filter with a bandwidth that is equivalent to the transmission bandwidth.

**THE CORRECT ANSWER IS: (C)**

**540.** Determine the relative power amplitudes of multipath components at $\tau = 0, 1, 4$, and 6 microseconds (μs).

From the graph:

$P_r(\tau) = -10$ dB at $\tau = 0$

$10 \log_{10} P = -10$ dB (at $\tau = 0$) so $P = 0.1$

$\tau = 0; \quad P = 0.1$

Similarly:

$\tau = 1 \, \mu s; \qquad P = 1$

$\tau = 4 \, \mu s; \qquad P = 0.001$

$\tau = 6 \, \mu s; \qquad P = 0.01$

$$\overline{\tau} \, (\mu s) = \frac{\sum\limits_{k} P(\tau_k)\tau_k}{\sum\limits_{k} P(\tau_k)}$$

$$= \frac{0.1(0) + 1(1) + 0.001(4) + 0.01(6)}{0.1 + 1 + 0.001 + 0.01}$$

$$= \frac{1 + 0.004 + 0.06}{1.111} = \frac{1.064}{1.111}$$

$$= 0.96 \, \mu s$$

**THE CORRECT ANSWER IS: (A)**